A-LEVEL YEAR 2

STUDENT GUIDE

WJEC/Eduqas

Biology

Energy, homeostasis and the environment
(WJEC)

Energy for life
Requirements for life (Eduqas)

Andy Clarke

Philip Allan, an imprint of Hodder Education, an Hachette UK company, Blenheim Court, George Street, Banbury, Oxfordshire OX16 5BH

Orders

Hachette UK Distribution, Hely Hutchinson Centre, Milton Road, Didcot, Oxfordshire, OX11 7HH

tel: 01235 827827

e-mail: education@hachette.co.uk

Lines are open 9.00 a.m.–5.00 p.m., Monday to Friday. You can also order through the Hodder Education website: www.hoddereducation.co.uk

ISBN 978-1-4718-5934-2

First printed 2016

Impression number 5 4 3

Year 2021

Cover photo: skampixelle/Fotolia; p. 79: Wayne Faberberg/UNH/Visuals Unlimited/Corbis

Typeset by Integra Software Services Pvt. Ltd, Pondicherry, India

Printed and bound by CPI Group (UK) Ltd, Croydon, CR0 4YY

Hachette UK's policy is to use papers that are natural, renewable and recyclable products and made from wood grown in well-managed forests and other controlled sources. The logging and manufacturing processes are expected to conform to the environmental regulations of the country of origin.

Contents

Content Guidance

Questions & Answers

Getting the most from this book

Exam tips

Advice on key points in the text to help you learn and recall content, avoid pitfalls, and polish your exam technique in order to boost your grade.

Knowledge check

Rapid-fire questions throughout the Content Guidance section to check your understanding.

Knowledge check answers

1 Turn to the back of the book for the Knowledge check answers.

Summaries

- Each core topic is rounded off by a bullet-list summary for quick-check reference of what you need to know.

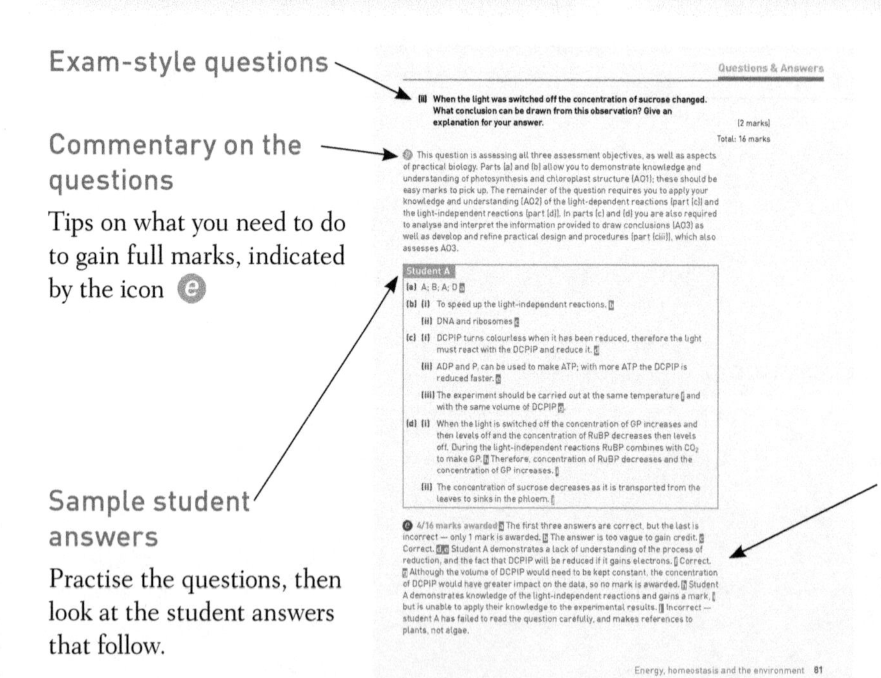

Questions & Answers

(ii) When the light was switched off the concentration of sucrose changed. What conclusion can be drawn from this observation? Give an explanation for your answer. (2 marks)

Total: 16 marks

This question is assessing all three assessment objectives, as well as aspects of practical biology. Parts (a) and (b) allow you to demonstrate knowledge and understanding of photosynthesis and chloroplast structure (AO1); these should be easy marks to pick up. The remainder of the question requires you to apply your knowledge and understanding (AO2) of the light-dependent reactions (part (c)) and the light-independent reactions (part (d)). In parts (c) and (d) you are also required to analyse and interpret the information provided to draw conclusions (AO3) as well as develop and refine practical design and procedures (part (ciii)), which also assesses AO3.

Student A

(a) A; B; A; D [a]

(b) (i) To speed up the light-independent reactions. [b]

(ii) DNA and ribosomes [c]

(c) (i) DCPIP turns colourless when it has been reduced, therefore the light must react with the DCPIP and reduce it. [d]

(ii) ADP and P, can be used to make ATP; with more ATP the DCPIP is reduced faster. [e]

(iii) The experiment should be carried out at the same temperature [f] and with the same volume of DCPIP [g].

(d) (i) When the light is switched off the concentration of GP increases and then levels off and the concentration of RuBP decreases then levels off. During the light-independent reactions RuBP combines with CO_2 to make GP. [h] Therefore, concentration of RuBP decreases and the concentration of GP increases. [i]

(ii) The concentration of sucrose decreases as it is transported from the leaves to sinks in the phloem. [j]

4/16 marks awarded [a] The first three answers are correct, but the last is incorrect — only 1 mark is awarded. [b] The answer is too vague to gain credit. [c] Correct. [d/e] Student A demonstrates a lack of understanding of the process of reduction, and the fact that DCPIP will be reduced if it gains electrons. [f] Correct. [g] Although the volume of DCPIP would need to be kept constant, the concentration of DCPIP would have greater impact on the data, so no mark is awarded. [h] Student A demonstrates knowledge of the light-independent reactions and gains a mark, [i] but is unable to apply their knowledge to the experimental results. [j] Incorrect — student A has failed to read the question carefully, and makes references to plants, not algae.

Energy, homeostasis and the environment 81

Exam-style questions

Commentary on the questions

Tips on what you need to do to gain full marks, indicated by the icon e

Sample student answers

Practise the questions, then look at the student answers that follow.

Commentary on sample student answers

Read the comments (preceded by the icon e) showing how many marks each answer would be awarded in the exam and exactly how and where marks are gained or lost.

About this book

WJEC specification

This guide will help you to prepare for the **WJEC A2 Biology Unit 3: Energy, homeostasis and the environment** exam. Your knowledge and understanding of some of the principles in Units 1 and 2 may be re-examined here as well.

The **Content Guidance** covers all the concepts you need to understand and facts you need to know for the Unit 3 exam. It also includes *exam tips* and *knowledge checks* to help you prepare for Unit 3.

Eduqas specification

This guide will help you to prepare for the **Eduqas Biology Component 1: Energy for life** exam and **Component 3: Requirements for life** exam. Your knowledge and understanding of some of the core concepts may also be assessed in these papers.

The **Content Guidance** covers all the concepts you need to understand and facts you need to know for the Component 1 exam. However, it only covers two out of the five topics you need to know for the Component 3 exam. The content of the other three topics can be found in the second student guide in this series. The content covering the option modules can be found in the fourth student guide in this series.

This section also includes *exam tips* and *knowledge checks* to help you prepare for these exams.

The order in which topics appear in the guide follows the order of the specification, with the exception of 'Importance of ATP'. This deals with the synthesis of ATP via chemiosmosis, which is included in the sections on photosynthesis and respiration, thus placing the material in context.

Using this guide

The concepts in each topic are presented first followed by details of the processes and adaptations of the various structures involved. You are advised to familiarise yourself with the key ideas before attempting to learn the associated facts.

The A-level biology course is more demanding than AS. You have to develop a deeper understanding of biological concepts and demonstrate a greater ability to apply your knowledge and understanding of biology (AO2). The A-level course also has a greater synoptic element — you need to start piecing together the topics you have studied so far and try to see the links between them. In your first year of A-level you learned the 'core concepts' in biology — the fundamentals of biochemistry and cell biology. This knowledge underpins all aspects of A-level biology. To ensure that you have a good understanding of the topics covered in this guide it is essential that you revisit these concepts. Synoptic links are highlighted throughout the Content Guidance.

At the end of each topic is a brief description of the **practical work** that you should have undertaken during the course. In the majority of cases this provides opportunities for examiners to assess your **mathematical skills** as well as your practical skills. For example, when studying aspects of mammalian physiology, such as the kidney and the nervous system, you may have made observations of microscope slides of various tissues and organs. Examiners may use photomicrographs or drawings of these tissues and organs and ask questions relating the visible structures to their functions. They may also ask you to calculate the actual size of structures in the image, or to calculate the magnification of the image; both of which you should have done during your first A-level year.

The **Questions & Answers** section will help you to:

- familiarise yourself with many of the different question styles you can expect in the exam(s)
- understand what the examiners mean by terms like 'describe' and 'explain'
- interpret the question material — especially any data that the examiners give you
- write concise answers to the questions that the examiners set

Each question in this section is attempted by two students, student A and student B. Their answers, together with the examiner comments, should help you to see what you need to do to score a good mark — and how you can easily not score a good mark even though you probably understand the biology.

Content Guidance

Photosynthesis uses light energy to synthesise organic molecules

Green plants are autotrophic organisms that, during photosynthesis, synthesise complex organic molecules from simple inorganic molecules using light energy. Photosynthesis can be represented by the following simple chemical equation:

$$6CO_2 + 6H_2O \rightarrow C_6H_{12}O_6 + 6O_2$$

During photosynthesis light energy is converted into chemical energy in the form of organic molecules.

Photosynthesis takes place in the **chloroplasts** of plant cells. The main site of photosynthesis is the palisade tissue of the leaf. Chloroplasts are surrounded by a double membrane that encloses a fluid-filled stroma (Figure 1). Within the stroma is a series of flattened membrane-bound sacs called thylakoids, which form stacks called grana. These thylakoid membranes provide a very large surface area for the absorption of light energy.

Exam tip

The majority of life on Earth is dependent upon photosynthesis:

- It converts light energy into chemical energy that can be used by other organisms.
- It provides a source of complex organic molecules for heterotrophic organisms.
- It releases oxygen, which is necessary for aerobic respiration.

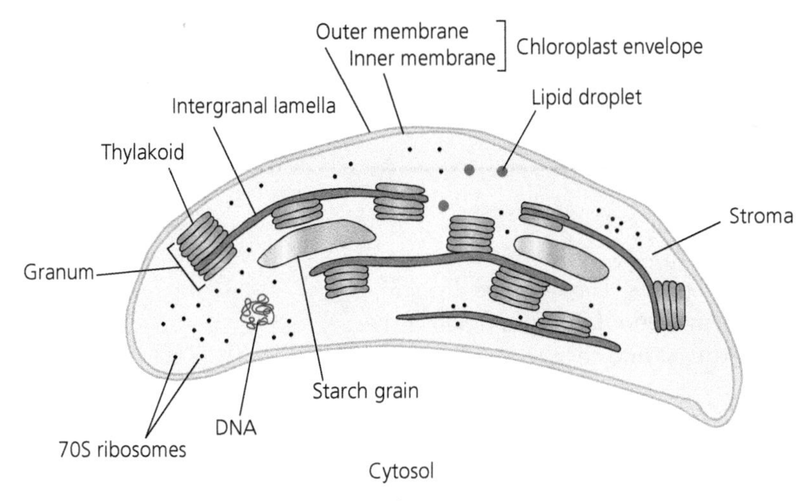

Figure 1 The structure of a chloroplast

There are two main stages in photosynthesis: the **light-dependent stage** and the **light-independent stage**. In the light-dependent stage:

- Photosynthetic pigments (e.g. chlorophyll) absorb light energy, which results in the loss of electrons. The electrons are transferred to an electron acceptor.

- The energy absorbed by the electrons is then released via a series of redox reactions and used to synthesise ATP from ADP and P_i (**photophosphorylation**) and to reduce the coenzyme NADP to $NADPH_2$.
- Light energy is converted into **chemical energy** within the organic molecules ATP and $NADPH_2$.

Photophosphorylation A process involving the synthesis of ATP using light energy.

Synoptic link to biological molecules: Starch grains are found in chloroplasts. Within the stroma molecules of glucose undergo condensation reactions to form starch. Therefore, there must be an enzyme in the stroma that catalyses these reactions.

The light-independent stage involves a series of enzyme-catalysed reactions in which carbon dioxide is reduced to form a carbohydrate. This requires $NADPH_2$ and energy released from the hydrolysis of ATP.

Figure 2 shows an overview of the two main stages in photosynthesis occurring within a chloroplast.

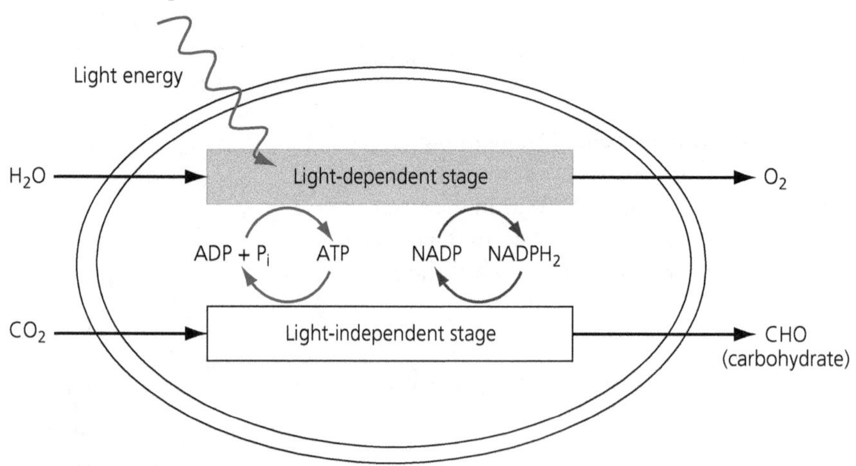

Figure 2 Outline of the stages of photosynthesis

Photosynthetic pigments

There are several photosynthetic pigments found in plants. These can be divided into two main groups, the **chlorophylls** and the **carotenoids**. The function of these pigments is to absorb light energy, thereby converting it into chemical energy.

Absorption and action spectra

The **absorption spectrum** (Figure 3a) shows the percentage of light absorbed by a particular pigment at different wavelengths of light. The **action spectrum** (Figure 3b) shows the rate of photosynthesis at different wavelengths of light. Since the two graphs show a similar trend, it suggests that these pigments are those responsible for the absorption of the wavelengths of light used in photosynthesis.

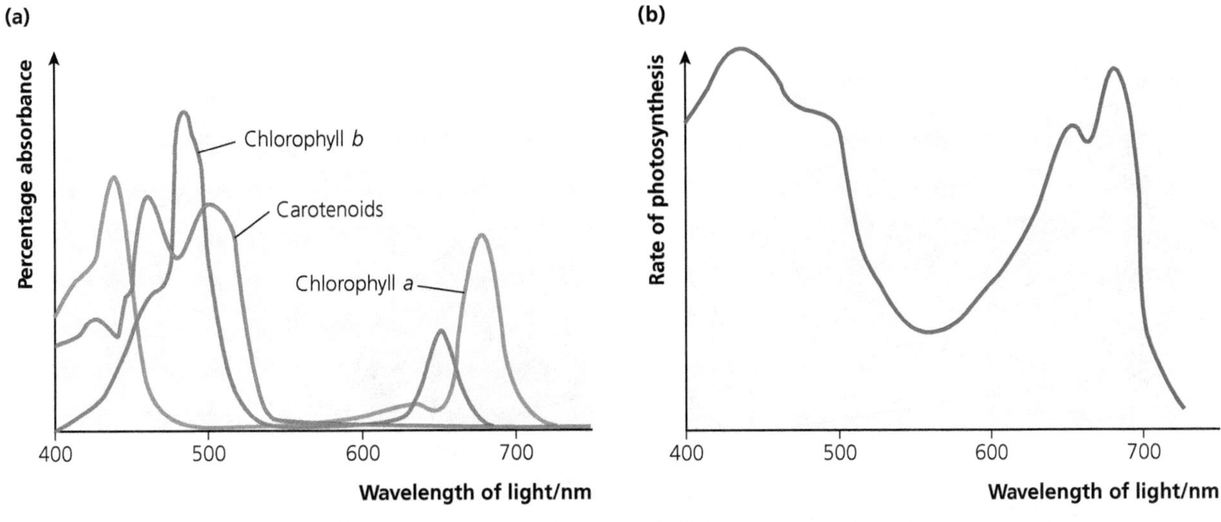

Figure 3 (a) Absorption spectra for photosynthesis pigments. (b) The action spectrum for photosynthesis

From the absorption spectrum it can be seen that:

- chlorophyll molecules absorb wavelengths of light in the blue-violet and red regions of the visible spectrum
- the peak absorptions for chlorophyll *a* and chlorophyll *b* differ slightly
- the carotenoids (e.g. xanthophyll and beta carotene) absorb wavelengths of light in the blue-violet region

Photosystems

It can be seen from Figure 4 that the photosynthetic pigments are arranged in clusters embedded in the **thylakoid membranes** of the chloroplasts. These clusters are known as **photosystems**. A photosystem consists of an antenna complex and a reaction centre (Figure 5).

In a photosystem, **chlorophyll *a*** is the main photosynthetic pigment and is found in the reaction centre. **Chlorophyll *b*** and the **carotenoids** are accessory pigments found in the antenna complex. The molecules in the complex are arranged so as to channel light energy to the reaction centre.

There are two types of photosystem:

- In **photosystem I** the reaction centre is called P700 as it contains two chlorophyll *a* molecules with a maximum absorption at a wavelength of 700 nm.
- In **photosystem II** the reaction centre is called P680 as it contains two chlorophyll *a* molecules with a maximum absorption at a wavelength of 680 nm.

Exam tip

Synoptic link to leaf structure: You learned about the structure of chloroplasts and their distribution in the leaves of angiosperms in A-level year 1. It would be wise to review your notes on these to ensure you understand the links. You may be given electron micrographs or drawings of chloroplasts and asked to identify the different structures or the locations of different parts of photosynthesis.

Exam tip

At A-level you are expected to use the correct terminology when answering questions. You will not gain credit for vague statements such as 'chlorophyll absorbs light' or 'chlorophyll absorbs blue-violet light'. You must refer to chlorophyll absorbing light energy or wavelengths of light in the blue-violet region of the spectrum.

Knowledge check 1

Explain the advantage to a plant of having chloroplasts that contain several different light-absorbing pigments.

Knowledge check 2

Explain why plants appear green.

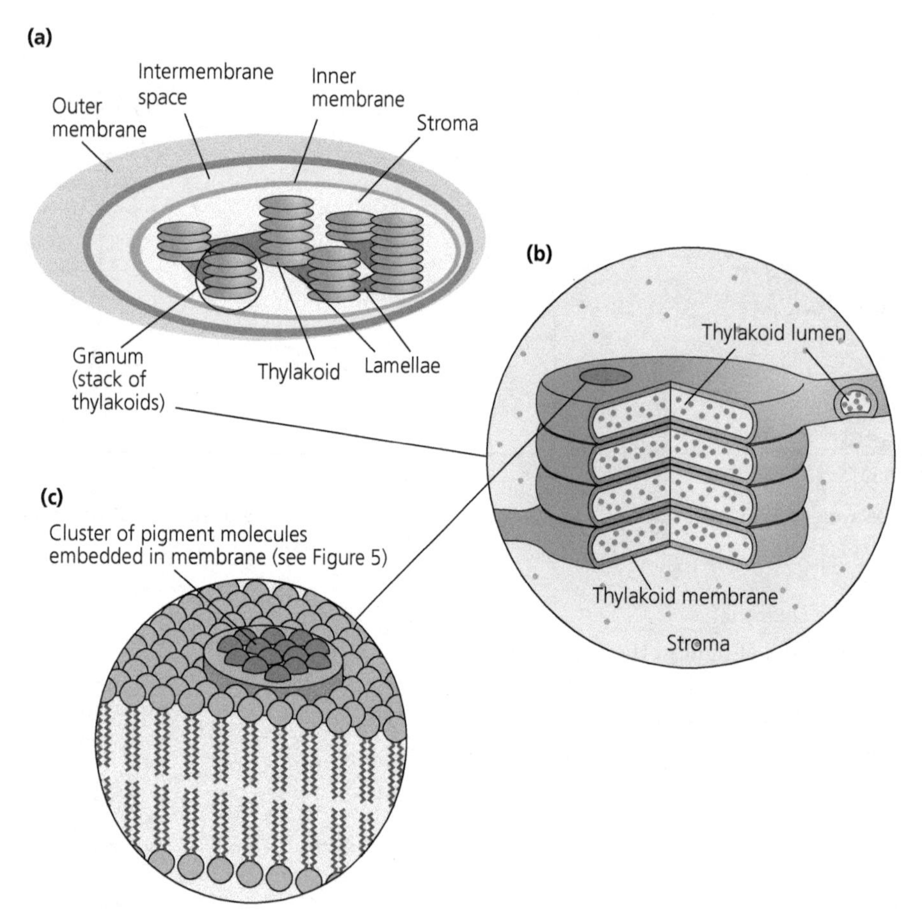

Figure 4 (a) The structure of a chloroplast. (b) A section through a single thylakoid. (c) Pigments in a thylakoid membrane

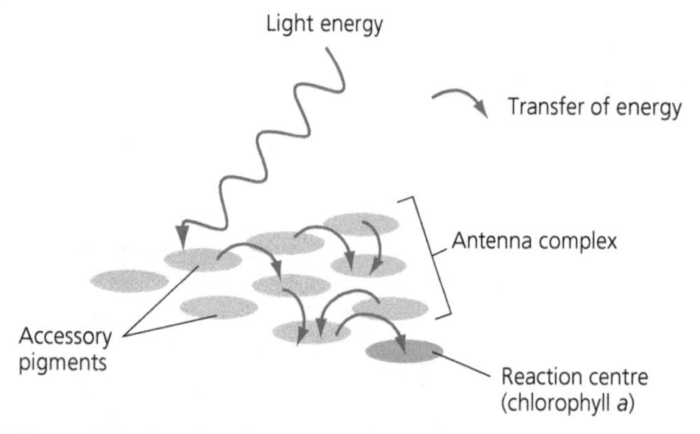

Figure 5 A photosystem

The light-dependent stage

The light-dependent stage involves the formation of ATP by photophosphorylation and the reduction of the coenzyme NADP. These events are summarised in a diagram, known as the 'Z-scheme', shown in Figure 6.

Knowledge check 3

State exactly where in the chloroplast you would expect to find photosystems.

Knowledge check 4

Photosystems contain several pigments. State the location of the following pigments within a photosystem:

a chlorophyll *a*
b chlorophyll *b*

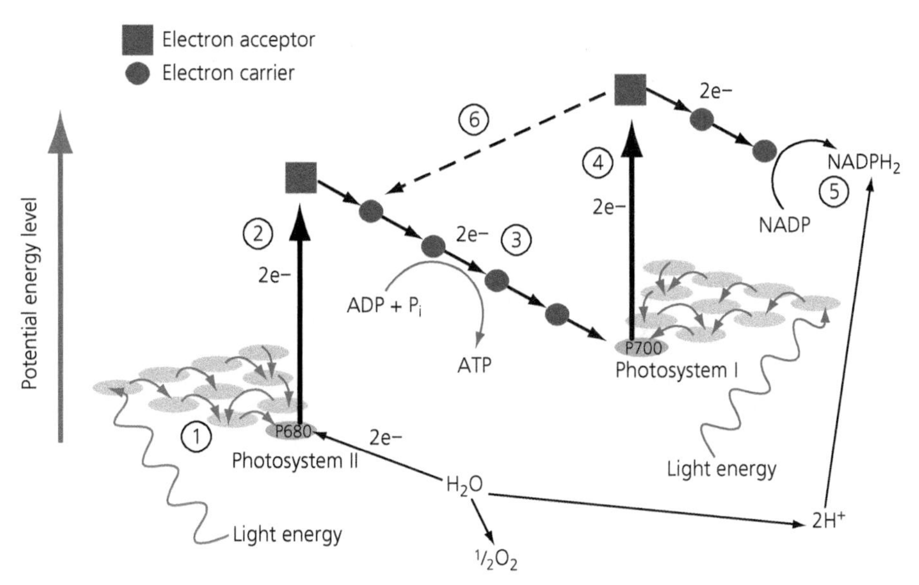

Figure 6 The light-dependent stage (the 'Z-scheme')

1. Photosynthetic pigments in the antenna complex of photosystem II absorb light energy. The energy is transferred to the reaction centre where it excites an electron in each of the two chlorophyll *a* molecules.
2. The excited electrons are boosted to a higher energy level. They leave the chlorophyll *a* molecules and are received by an electron acceptor; this oxidises the chlorophyll *a* molecules while reducing the electron acceptor.
3. The electrons are passed along the electron transport chain in a series of redox reactions to photosystem I, which is at a lower energy level. The energy lost by the electrons is used to convert ADP and P_i to ATP — this is photophosphorylation.
4. Light absorbed by photosystem I boosts two electrons from the chlorophyll *a* molecules in the reaction centre to an even higher energy level. The electrons are received by another electron acceptor.
5. Electrons (from the chlorophyll *a* molecules) and H^+ (from the photolysis of water) are used to reduce NADP (the final electron acceptor) to $NADPH_2$.

Photolysis of water

This occurs at stage 1 of the light-dependent reactions. The electrons removed from the chlorophyll *a* molecules in photosystem II are replaced by electrons (e^-) from a water molecule. The loss of electrons from the water molecule causes it to dissociate into protons (H^+) and oxygen — this is known as **photolysis**.

Chemiosmotic theory of photophosphorylation

Figure 7 shows how ATP is synthesised during non-cyclic photophosphorylation. As the electrons pass along the electron transport chain they lose energy. This energy is used to pump protons (H^+) from the stroma, across the thylakoid membrane and into the thylakoid space. The protons accumulate so that steep

Exam tip

NADP is the coenzyme involved in photosynthesis. Do not confuse it with NAD, which is involved in respiration. Remember that the letter 'p' is in both NAD**P** and **p**hotosynthesis.

Exam tip

The electrons lost from the chlorophyll *a* molecule in photosystem I are used to reduce NADP. These electrons are replaced by those lost by the chlorophyll *a* molecule in photosystem II, which are in turn replaced by those lost by the water molecule during photolysis.

concentration and electrochemical gradients are established between the thylakoid space and the stroma. These gradients are also maintained by:

- the photolysis of water, which occurs in the thylakoid space and increases the H^+ concentration
- the reduction of NADP, which occurs in the stroma and decreases the H^+ concentration

The protons (H^+) diffuse back into the stroma through the chemiosmotic protein channels where the enzyme ATP synthase is located. The flow of protons through ATP synthase provides the energy required to produce ATP from ADP and P_i.

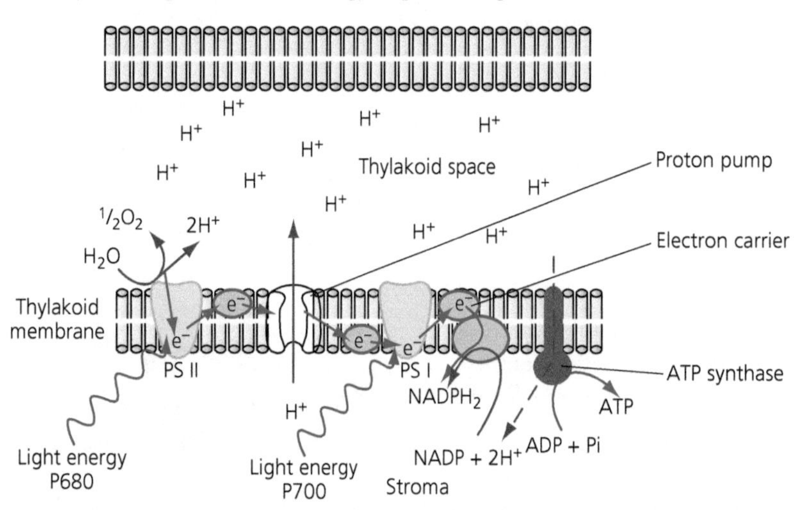

Figure 7 Chemiosmosis and non-cyclic photophosphorylation

Electrons from the chlorophyll *a* molecules in photosystem I are used to reduce NADP and are replaced indirectly by electrons from the photolysis of water. This is known as **non-cyclic phosphorylation** and is represented by stages 1 to 5 in Figure 6.

You can see from Figure 6 that the electron acceptor at stage 4 is at the highest energy state. It is possible for some of these excited electrons to return to the chlorophyll *a* molecule in photosystem I via the electron transport chain. This is known as **cyclic phosphorylation** and is represented by stages 4, 6 and 3 in Figure 6.

Cyclic and non-cyclic photophosphorylation are compared in Table 1.

Table 1 Cyclic and non-cyclic phosphorylation

Feature	Cyclic photophosphorylation	Non-cyclic photophosphorylation
Photosystems involved	I only	I and II
Photolysis of water	No	Yes
Electron donor	Chlorophyll *a* in photosystem I	Chlorophyll *a* in photosystem I
Terminal electron acceptor	Chlorophyll *a* in photosystem I	NADP
Products	ATP	ATP, $NADPH_2$ and oxygen

The light-independent stage (Calvin cycle)

The light-independent reactions take place in the stroma of the chloroplast because this is where the enzymes involved are located. During these reactions ATP and $NADPH_2$ (from the light-dependent stage) are used to reduce carbon dioxide to triose phosphate (a 3C carbohydrate). Figure 8 shows the main stages in the Calvin cycle.

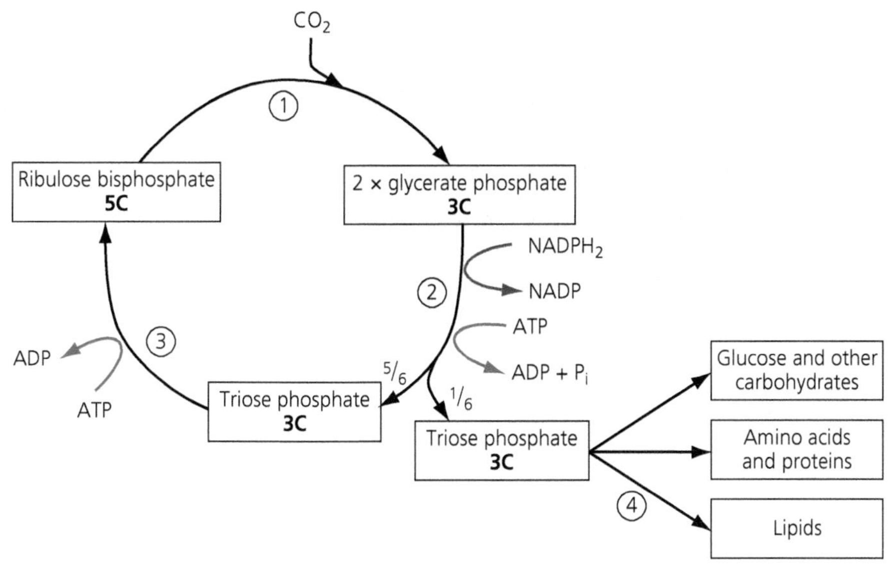

Figure 8 The steps involved in the light-independent stage (the Calvin cycle)

1. Carbon dioxide combines with ribulose bisphosphate (RuBP) to form two molecules of glycerate-3-phosphate (GP), which is the first product of photosynthesis. This reaction is a carboxylation (addition of carbon dioxide) reaction and is catalysed by the enzyme **rubisco** (ribulose bisphosphate carboxylase). As carbon dioxide is converted from an inorganic form into an organic molecule the process is also referred to as **carbon fixation**.
2. $NADPH_2$ is used to reduce the two molecules of glycerate-3-phosphate into two molecules of triose phosphate (TP). The hydrolysis of ATP provides the energy for this reaction.
3. Most of the TP (five out of six molecules) is converted by a series of reactions, via ribulose phosphate, into RuBP. ATP supplies the phosphate and energy required.
4. Some of the TP (one of the six molecules) is converted rapidly to glucose and other carbohydrates, amino acids, lipids and nucleic acids.

Exam tip

Balancing the equation:

$$6CO_2 + 6H_2O \rightarrow C_6H_{12}O_6 + 6O_2$$

For every molecule of CO_2 that enters the Calvin cycle two molecules of triose phosphate (TP) are produced. Six molecules of CO_2 entering the cycle will result in the production of 12 molecules of TP of which two molecules will leave the cycle and combine to form one molecule of glucose.

Exam tip

Five triose phosphate molecules contain 15 carbon atoms and 5 phosphate groups. Three ribulose bisphosphate molecules also contain 15 carbon atoms but 6 phosphate groups. The hydrolysis of ATP supplies the extra phosphate group during these reactions.

Knowledge check 5

Name the two products from the light-dependent stage that are required for the Calvin cycle.

Investigating photosynthesis: Calvin's lollipop

Melvin Calvin was an American biochemist who investigated the pathway by which carbon dioxide is converted into organic compounds during photosynthesis. A suspension of the unicellular alga *Chlorella* was placed in a flattened glass vessel that was called the 'lollipop' (Figure 9a). The suspension of *Chlorella* was supplied with radioactive carbon dioxide. The lollipop was illuminated and the algae allowed to photosynthesise. As the *Chlorella* photosynthesised, the radioactive carbon dioxide was 'fixed' and incorporated into organic molecules (the intermediate compounds), which became radioactive. At specific time intervals samples of the *Chlorella* were released into boiling alcohol. This denatured enzymes, killed the *Chlorella* and stopped the light-independent reactions at a particular point in time.

Compounds that the radioactive carbon had reached at a particular moment were determined by chromatography and autoradiography (Figure 9b). The order in which each compound is produced was found by identifying the molecules and analysing the results. From these results Calvin discovered the metabolic pathway that is now known as the light-independent stage of photosynthesis.

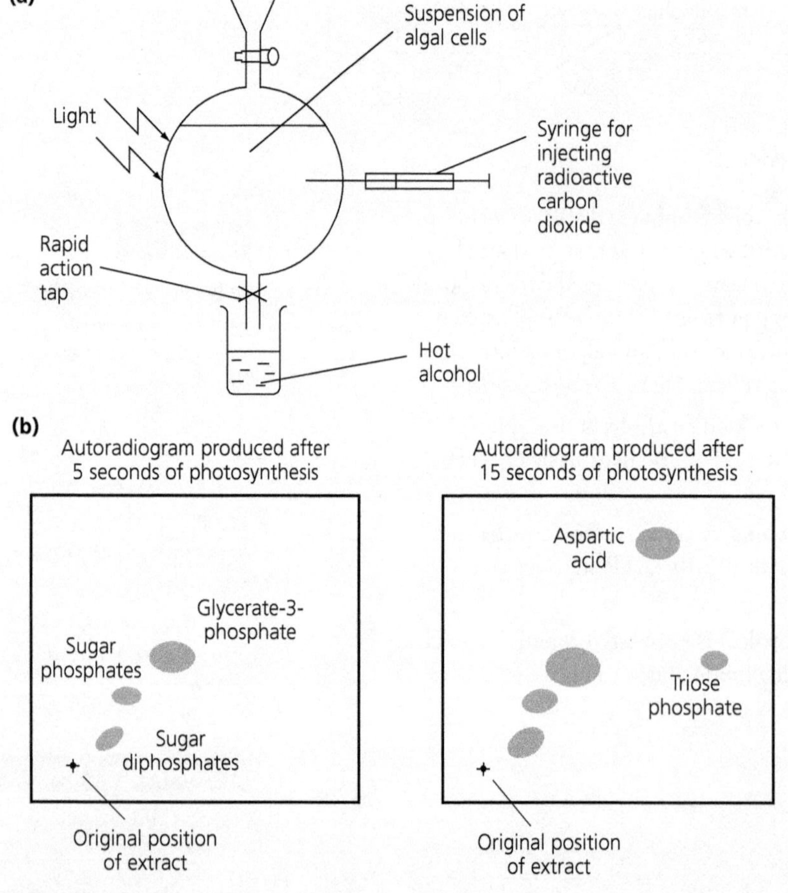

Figure 9 (a) Calvin's lollipop. (b) Autoradiograms showing the different molecules synthesised during Calvin's experiments

Practical work

Chromatography

Chromatography is a technique for **separating molecules** from a mixture. It relies on the principle that different molecules have differing solubility in particular solvents.

A pestle and mortar can be used to obtain an extract of photosynthetic pigments from plant tissue. A concentrated spot of this extract is then applied to the origin of the chromatogram. When the end of the chromatogram is placed into a solvent the molecules will then separate out according to their solubility/molecular mass. More soluble/lighter molecules move further up the chromatogram than the less soluble/heavier molecules (Figure 10).

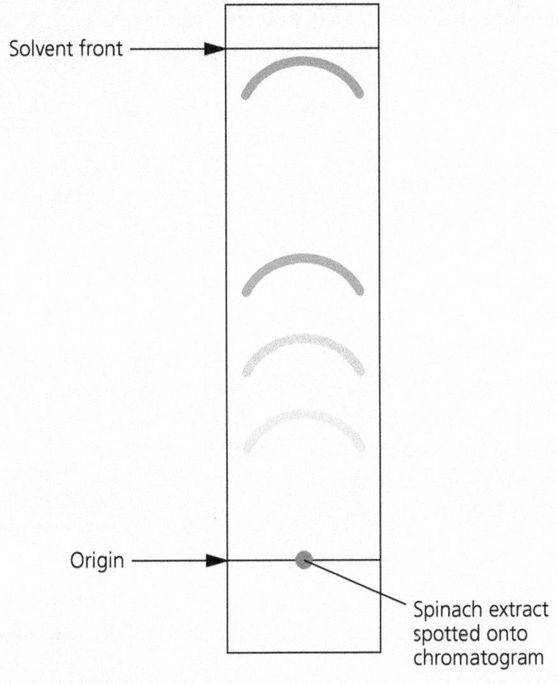

Figure 10 Chromatogram showing the different photosynthetic pigments

Once the molecules have been separated they can be identified by calculating their Rf value. The Rf value is specific to each molecule and compares the distance travelled by the molecule with that of the solvent.

$$Rf = \frac{\text{distance travelled by the molecule}}{\text{distance travelled by the solvent front}}$$

Pigment	Rf value
Xanthophyll	0.28
Chlorophyll *b*	0.42
Chlorophyll *a*	0.59
Carotene	0.98

Exam tip

When calculating Rf values you must measure the distance travelled by both the molecule and the solvent front from the origin. Rf values are always less than 1; if you get an answer above 1 then you have reversed the calculation.

Knowledge check 6

a Use Figure 10 to calculate the Rf value of the yellow pigment.

b Use the table of Rf values on the left to identify the four molecules.

Factors that affect the rate of photosynthesis

The rate of photosynthesis can be affected by both internal and external factors. Internal factors include the type and concentration of photosynthetic pigments and enzymes present. External factors include light intensity, the wavelength of light, the concentration of CO_2, temperature and the availability of water and mineral ions, such as nitrates and magnesium.

Internal factors are difficult to manipulate but external factors, such as light intensity, CO_2 concentration and temperature, can be easily manipulated to investigate the rate of photosynthesis in plants or algae. These investigations also demonstrate the **law of limiting factors**.

Law of limiting factors
This states that the rate of any physiological process will be limited by the factor that is in shortest supply. Any change in the level of a limiting factor will affect the rate of reaction.

To investigate the effect of light intensity on the rate of photosynthesis a lamp can be placed at varying distances from an aquatic plant, such as *Elodea*, and the volume of oxygen produced in a fixed time period could be measured. The results from this investigation would look similar to the graph in Figure 11.

Exam tip

As there are many factors that influence the rate of photosynthesis it is important to try to control all other variables during each investigation. In this experiment the temperature could be controlled using a water-bath and the CO_2 concentration could be controlled by adding a fixed mass of $NaHCO_3$ to the boiling tube containing *Elodea*. However, it is impossible to control internal factors, such as the concentrations of chlorophyll and rubisco. By choosing plants of the same species, the same age, with the same number of leaves you can *assume* that these variables will be the same. Inevitably you will get variation within your repeat data, and this could be due to variations in these internal factors.

Exam tip

Synoptic links to biological molecules: Plants require **magnesium** to synthesise chlorophyll. Magnesium deficiency leads to chlorosis and death. Plants also require nitrogen to synthesise amino acids, nucleic acids and chlorophyll from triose phosphate. Plants obtain their nitrogen as nitrates (NO_3^-) or ammonium ions (NH_4^+) from the soil (this is also a synoptic link to the nitrogen cycle).

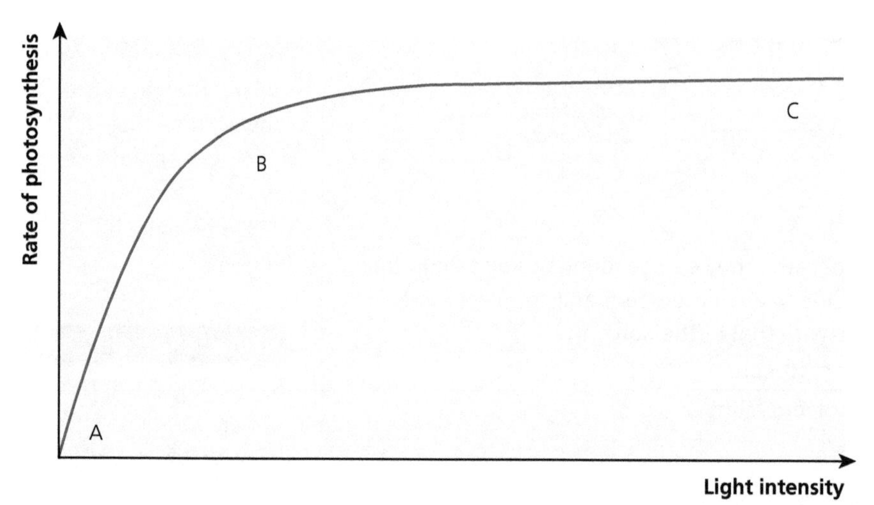

Figure 11 Graph showing the effect of light intensity on the rate of photosynthesis

Figure 11 shows that as the light intensity increases, the rate of photosynthesis also increases and then levels off. Between points A and B, light intensity increases, and so does the rate of photosynthesis. This implies that light intensity must be the limiting factor on the rate of photosynthesis. However, as there is no further increase in the rate of photosynthesis between points B and C, light intensity can no longer be limiting the rate. Therefore, some other factor, for example the temperature, concentration of CO_2, or concentration of rubisco, is limiting the rate of photosynthesis.

Summary

After studying this topic you should be able to demonstrate and apply your knowledge and understanding of:

- the distribution of chloroplasts in relation to light absorption
- the role of chloroplasts as transducers in the conversion of light energy into the chemical energy of ATP
- the relationship between the absorption and action spectra
- the arrangement of photosynthetic pigments within photosystems and energy transfer to reaction centres
- the process of cyclic and non-cyclic photophosphorylation including:
  - the source of electrons for the electron transport chain
  - photolysis of water as a source of electrons for photosystem II
  - the reduction of NADP by the addition of electrons and protons
- the synthesis of ATP by means of a flow of protons through the enzyme ATP synthase by chemiosmosis
- the reactions occurring in the light-independent stage, including:
  - the role of $NADPH_2$ as a source of reducing power and ATP as a source of energy for the reactions
  - the uptake of carbon dioxide and the role of rubisco
  - the fate of triose phoshate
- the role of magnesium and nitrogen in plant metabolism and the concept of limiting factors

Respiration releases chemical energy in biological processes

Respiration is a process that occurs within the cells of all living organisms. It can be represented by the following simple chemical equation:

$$C_6H_{12}O_6 + 6O_2 \rightarrow 6CO_2 + 6H_2O$$

Organic molecules, such as glucose and fatty acids, contain high-energy C–C, C–H and C–OH bonds. During respiration these organic molecules are oxidised to release energy in order to synthesise ATP from ADP and P_i.

There are three ways in which molecules can be oxidised or reduced:

	Oxidation	Reduction
1	Gaining oxygen	Losing oxygen
2	Losing hydrogen	Gaining hydrogen
3	Losing electrons (e^-)	Gaining electrons (e^-)

Exam tip

Synoptic link to nucleotides: In A-level year 1 you studied the structure of ATP and the importance of chemical energy in biological processes. Revisiting these topics will help you to understand energy transfers during respiration and the synthesis of ATP.

Oxidation and reduction reactions always take place together because as one molecule is oxidised so another molecule is reduced. These chemical reactions are called **redox** reactions. Figure 12 represents a typical step in the respiratory pathway. Note that the coenzyme (NAD) is reduced as the organic molecule is oxidised.

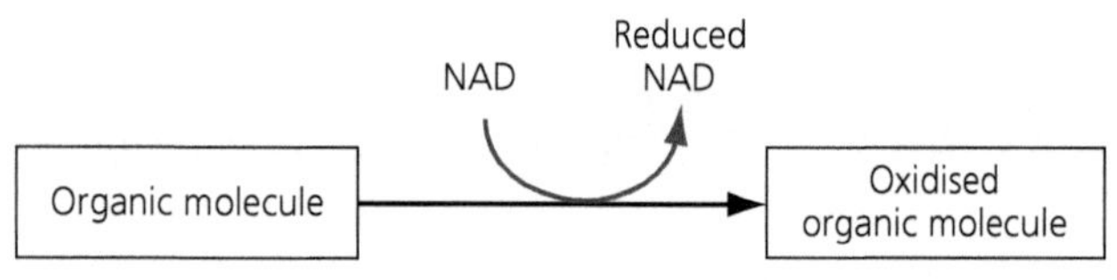

Figure 12 Oxidation of an organic molecule coupled with the reduction of a coenzyme

The oxidation reactions involved in respiration are exergonic (i.e. they release energy). The energy released from the organic molecule is used to reduce the coenzymes NAD and FAD, as these reactions are coupled. During each oxidation reaction a small quantity of energy is, in effect, transferred to these coenzymes.

During glycolysis, the link reaction and Krebs cycle organic molecules are repeatedly oxidised and therefore most of the energy contained within glucose is transferred to the reduced coenzymes $NADH_2$ and $FADH_2$. When they are re-oxidised the stored energy is used to synthesise ATP via **oxidative phosphorylation**.

This series of oxidation reactions in respiration brings about the gradual release of chemical energy from organic molecules in a series of small steps (as opposed to combustion, which is the uncontrolled release of energy in a single step).

Aerobic respiration occurs in the presence of oxygen. Respiration that takes place in the absence of oxygen is known as **anaerobic respiration**.

Exam tip

In biology it will be more helpful to you if you think about oxidation in terms of loss of hydrogen and loss of electrons and reduction in terms of gain of hydrogen and electrons.

Exam tip

Synoptic link to enzymes: Respiration is a series of enzyme-catalysed reactions. Therefore, factors that affect enzymes will affect the rate of respiration. The most important factor influencing the rate of respiration is temperature.

Aerobic respiration

Mitochondria are present in all eukaryotic cells and are involved in the synthesis of ATP during aerobic respiration. Figure 13 shows the structure of a mitochondrion. The organelle is composed of a double membrane enclosing a fluid-filled matrix. The inner membrane is highly folded to form cristae. This increases the surface area for the synthesis of ATP.

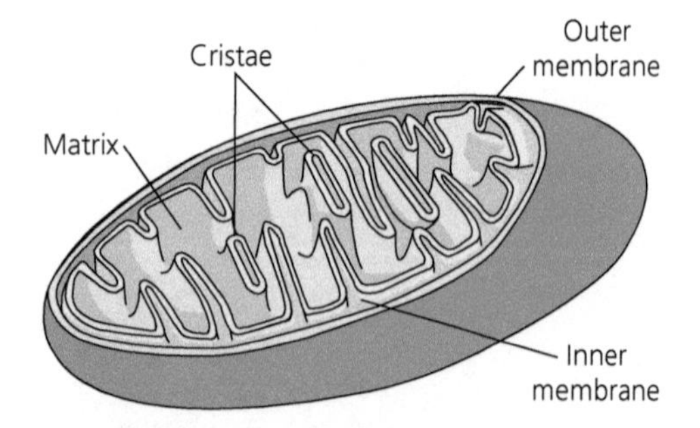

Figure 13 Structure of a mitochondrion

Figure 14 shows the location of the four stages of respiration. The diagram shows that ATP is synthesised mainly in the mitochondria.

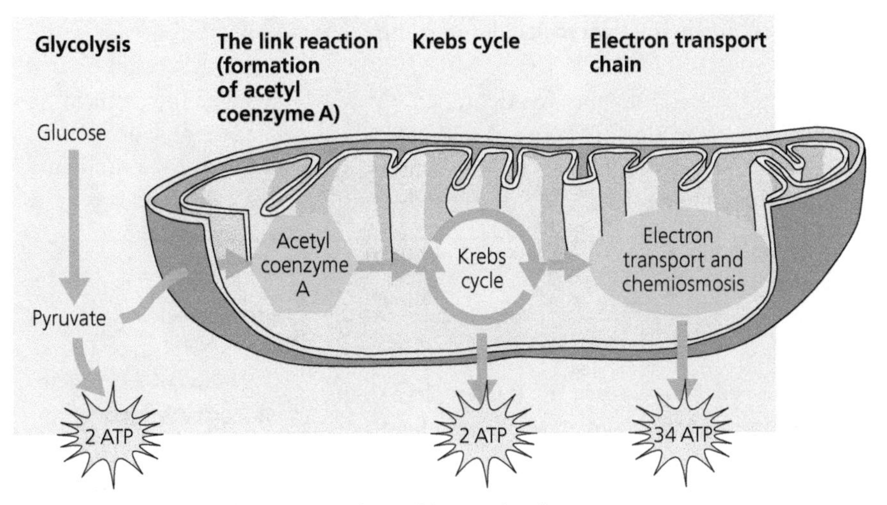

Figure 14 Outline of the stages of aerobic respiration

Glycolysis (splitting of glucose)

Glycolysis occurs in the cytoplasm — this is where the **enzymes** for glycolysis are located. The main stages in the pathway are shown in Figure 15.

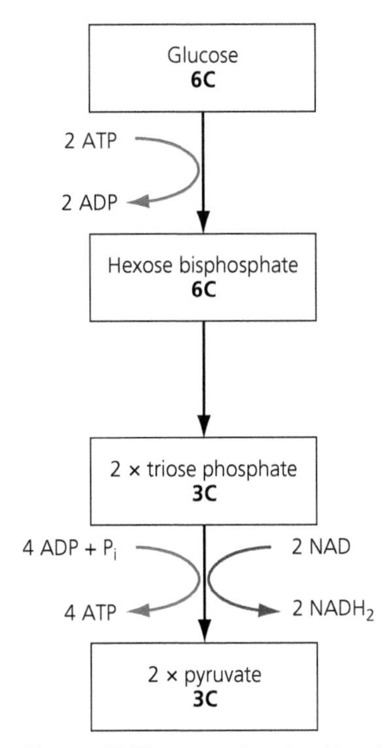

Figure 15 The steps involved in glycolysis

- **Step 1:** Two molecules of ATP are required for the **phosphorylation** of glucose to produce hexose bisphosphate. The energy released from the hydrolysis of ATP activates glucose and makes the molecule more reactive.

Exam tip

The 'law of conservation of energy' states that energy can neither be created nor destroyed. However energy can be converted from one form to another. When answering questions in relation to the hydrolysis of ATP, you must refer to energy being *released*. You will not gain any credit for stating that energy is produced.

- **Step 2:** Hexose bisphosphate is split (lysis), producing two molecules of triose phosphate (TP).
- **Step 3:** TP is **oxidised** via a dehydrogenation reaction into **pyruvate**. The hydrogen removed is used to reduce the coenzyme NAD to reduced NAD ($NADH_2$). The reaction is exergonic, and the energy released is used to synthesise four ATP molecules by substrate-level phosphorylation.

Glycolysis results in a net gain of *two ATP molecules* (two ATP molecules are used initially and four ATP molecules are synthesised).

Dehydrogenation reaction A reaction that involves the removal of pairs of hydrogen atoms from a molecule. It is catalysed by a dehydrogenase enzyme.

Substrate-level phosphorylation The synthesis of ATP using energy released from the breakdown of a high-energy substrate molecule.

The link reaction

Glycolysis links to the Krebs cycle via the **link reaction** (Figure 16). It takes place in the **mitochondrial matrix** (where the enzymes involved in the link reaction are found).

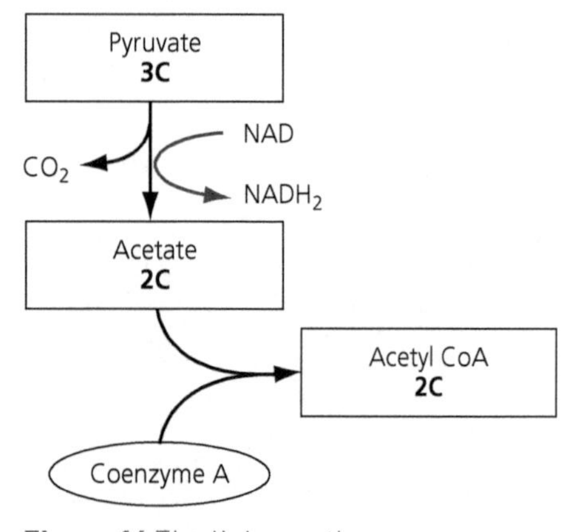

Figure 16 The link reaction

Knowledge check 7

Why is glycolysis referred to as being anaerobic?

Specific carrier proteins contained in the outer mitochondrial membrane transport pyruvate into the matrix. (Note that there are no glucose carrier proteins.) The pyruvate undergoes oxidative decarboxylation to form acetate (a 2C molecule). This involves:

- the **removal of hydrogen** (oxidation) to reduce the coenzyme NAD
- the **removal of a carboxyl group** (decarboxylation) to form carbon dioxide

The acetate combines with coenzyme-A to form **acetyl coenzyme-A**.

Two molecules of pyruvate enter the link reaction, so the reactions shown in Figures 16 and 17 only represent one-half of the reactions for the complete oxidation of one molecule of glucose.

Decarboxylation A reaction that involves the removal of a carboxyl group from a molecule resulting in the production of CO_2. It is catalysed by a decarboxylase enzyme.

Exam tip

It is important that you state the precise location within the cell where the different stages of respiration occur. You will not gain any credit for stating that the link reaction and Krebs cycle take place in the 'mitochondria' or the 'matrix' you must state it is in the mitochondrial matrix.

Krebs cycle

The Krebs cycle occurs in the **mitochondrial matrix** (this is where the correct enzymes are located). It involves a series of decarboxylation reactions and dehydrogenation reactions. Carbon dioxide, ATP and reduced coenzymes are produced (Figure 17).

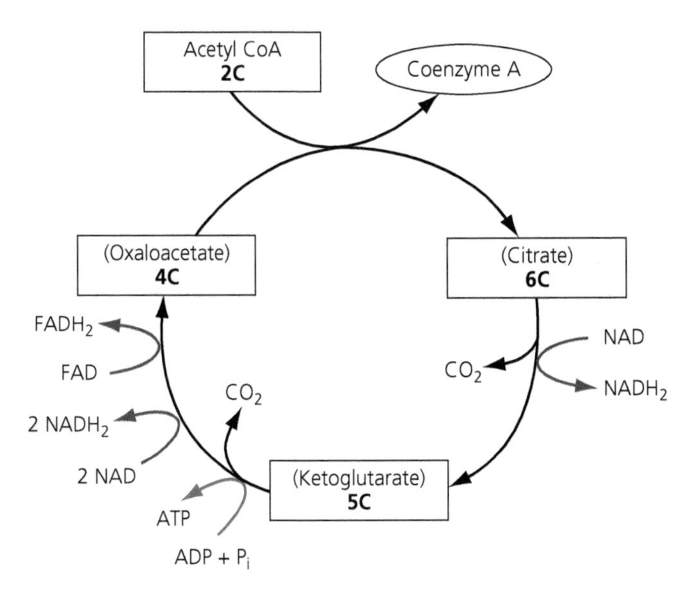

Figure 17 The steps involved in the Krebs cycle

Exam tip

Figure 17 shows the names of the intermediate molecules involved in the Krebs cycle. Although they may appear on the exam you are not expected to know them. What is important is that you understand what is being produced as these molecules are being recycled.

Knowledge check 8

Explain why carbon dioxide is not produced when glucose is added to a preparation of isolated mitochondria.

Acetyl coenzyme-A releases acetate (2C), which then combines with oxaloacetate (4C) to form citrate (6C). Citrate is then broken down in a series of oxidative decarboxylation reactions to regenerate oxaloacetate. These reactions involve:

- the loss of hydrogen (dehydrogenation/oxidation) and the loss of carbon dioxide (decarboxylation)
- the reduction of the coenzymes NAD and FAD to $NADH_2$ and $FADH_2$
- the production of ATP from ADP and P_i by substrate-level phosphorylation

The electron transport chain

The electron transport chain involves a chain of electron carriers that are located on the inner mitochondrial membrane (cristae). The cristae have a large surface area, so there are more electron carriers, which increases ATP synthesis. The reduced coenzymes, $NADH_2$ and $FADH_2$, produced during glycolysis, the link reaction and Krebs cycle act as a source of electrons and protons.

Figure 18 shows the electron carriers at progressively lower energy levels. As electrons pass along the chain of carriers, in a series of redox reactions, they release energy. This energy is used to synthesise ATP by **oxidative phosphorylation**. Oxygen is the terminal electron acceptor. It combines with protons (H^+) and electrons (e^-) and is reduced to water.

Oxidative phosphorylation The synthesis of ATP using energy released from redox reactions.

Figure 18 shows that for each $NADH_2$ entering the chain three ATP molecules are produced; each $FADH_2$ only generates two ATP molecules.

Chemiosmotic theory of oxidative phosphorylation

Figure 19 shows how ATP is synthesised during oxidative phosphorylation.

- The energy released from the electrons during the redox reactions is used to pump protons (H^+) from the matrix through the inner mitochondrial membrane into the inter-membrane space.

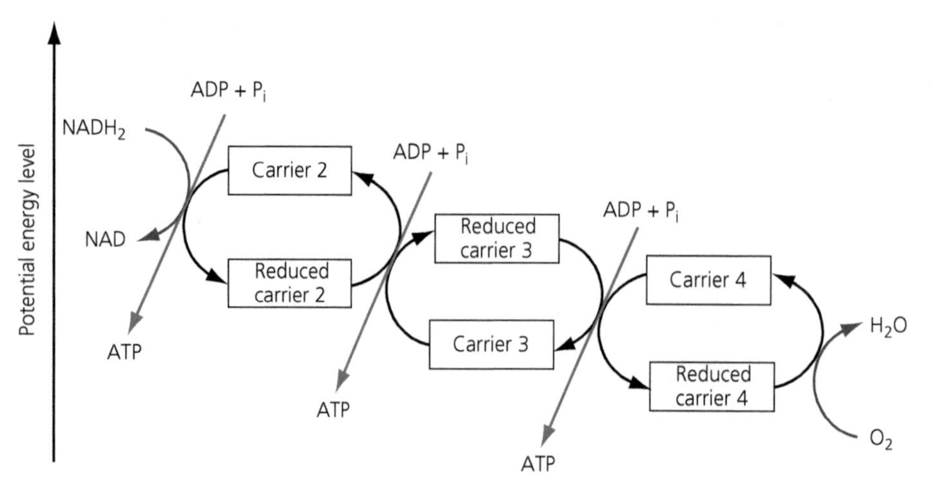

Figure 18 The electron transport chain

- The protons accumulate so that steep concentration and electrochemical gradients are established across the inner mitochondrial membrane.
- The inner membrane is impermeable to protons, so they can only diffuse back into the matrix via the stalked particles, which consist of a chemiosmotic channel protein attached to the enzyme **ATP synthase**.
- The flow of protons through the ATP synthase provides the energy required to produce ATP from ADP and P_i.

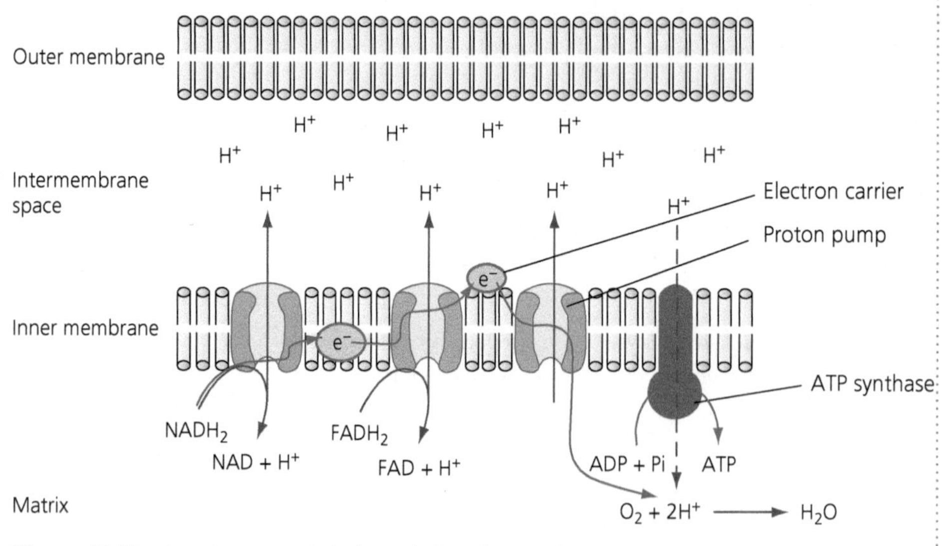

Figure 19 Electron transport chain and chemiosmosis

Each molecule of $NADH_2$ entering the chain results in three ATP molecules being synthesised as three proton pumps are involved. Each molecule of $FADH_2$ results in two ATP molecules being synthesised as only two proton pumps are involved.

Exam tip

Synoptic links to enzymes: Cyanide is a respiratory inhibitor. It is a **non-competitive inhibitor** of the enzyme cytochrome oxidase, which is associated with the final proton pump in the electron transport chain. When cyanide attaches to the enzyme the electron transport chain cannot function and oxidative phosphorylation cannot occur.

Knowledge check 9

Describe the role of oxygen in aerobic respiration.

Summary of aerobic respiration

Aerobic respiration involves the oxidation of glucose via a series of dehydrogenation reactions (Figure 20). Table 2 shows a summary of the molecules involved and the location of the different stages in aerobic respiration.

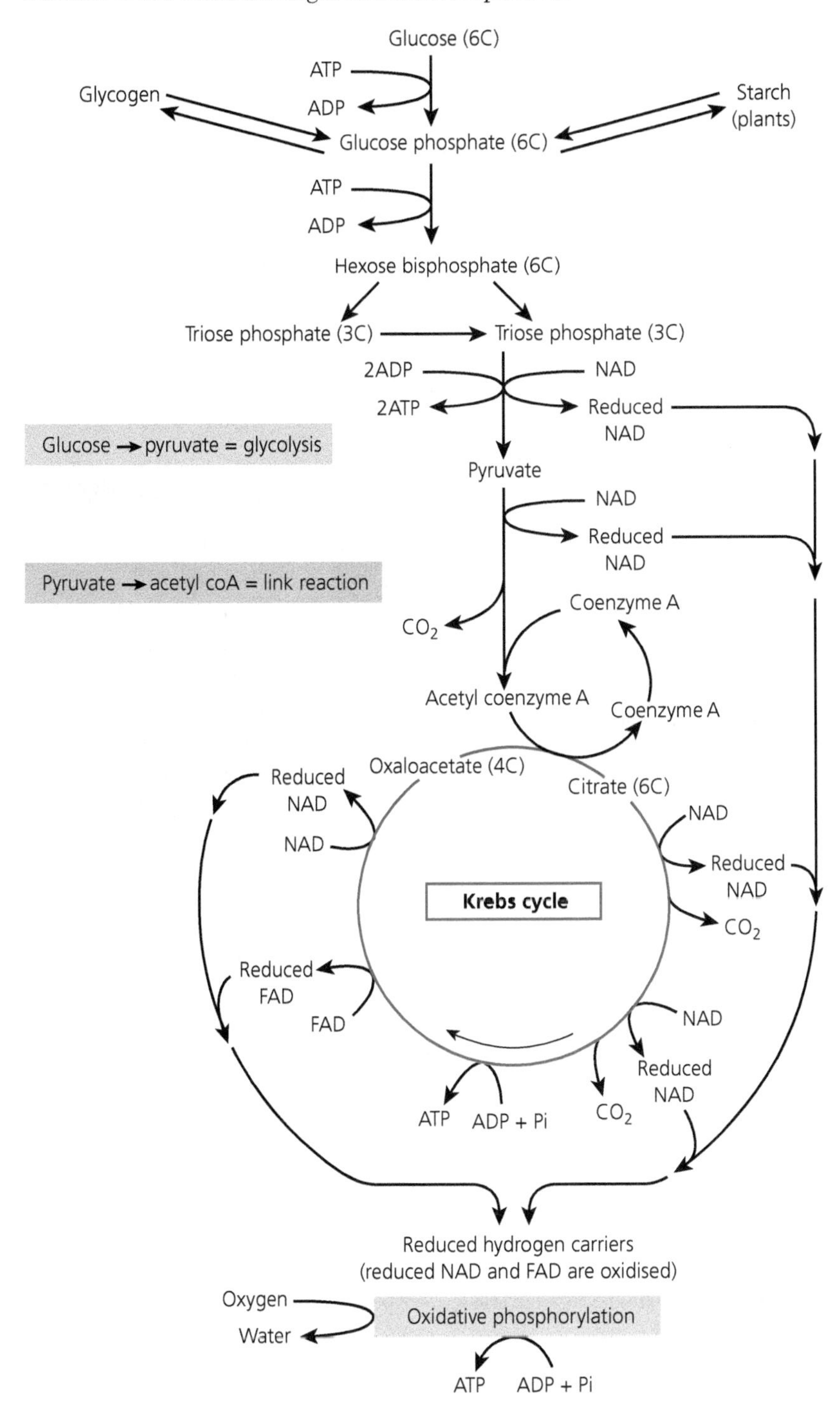

Figure 20 Summary of aerobic respiration

Table 2 Molecules involved and the location of the different stages in aerobic respiration

Stage in respiration	Precise location in the cell	Molecules required	Molecules produced
Glycolysis	Cytoplasm	Glucose, ATP, ADP and P_i, NAD	Pyruvate, ATP, $NADH_2$
Link reaction	Mitochondrial matrix	Pyruvate, NAD	Acetyl Co-A, $NADH_2$, CO_2
Krebs cycle	Mitochondrial matrix	Acetyl Co-A, ADP and P_i, NAD, FAD	CO_2, ATP, $NADH_2$, $FADH_2$
Electron transport chain	Inner mitochondrial membrane/cristae	$NADH_2$ and $FADH_2$, ADP and P_i, O_2	NAD and FAD, ATP, H_2O

Table 3 shows the number of ATP molecules produced via substrate-level phosphorylation and oxidative phosphorylation. The complete oxidation of one molecule of glucose can produce a maximum of 38 molecules of ATP:

- Four molecules of ATP (two from glycolysis and two from Krebs cycle) are produced by substrate-level phosphorylation.
- Thirty-four molecules of ATP are produced by oxidative phosphorylation.

Table 3 The ATP tally

Stages in aerobic respiration	(Net) number of molecules produced per glucose molecule		
	$NADH_2$	$FADH_2$	ATP
Glycolysis	2	0	2
Link reaction	2	0	0
Krebs cycle	6	2	2
Electron transport chain	The $NADH_2$ and $FADH_2$ supply the energy required to synthesise ATP: ■ The oxidation of 1 $NADH_2$ will result in 3 ATP being synthesised. ■ The oxidation of 1 $FADH_2$ will result in 2 ATP being synthesised.		34

Knowledge check 10

Apart from oxygen and carbon dioxide, name:

a two molecules that show a net movement into a mitochondrion

b two molecules that show a net movement out of a mitochondrion

Anaerobic respiration

Anaerobic respiration takes place in the cytoplasm of cells and occurs in the absence of oxygen. It is the incomplete breakdown of glucose. Without oxygen the electron transport chain cannot occur and $NADH_2$ and $FADH_2$ are not oxidised. NAD and FAD become limiting factors (i.e. they run out) and therefore the dehydrogenation reactions of the Krebs cycle and the link reaction can no longer occur. Glycolysis continues as the pyruvate enters a different pathway and is reduced, therefore oxidising $NADH_2$ to NAD. The pyruvate is converted to lactate in animals and ethanol in plants and fungi.

Figure 21 shows the anaerobic pathway in animals. Pyruvate is reduced by $NADH_2$ to form lactate. This recycles the NAD, which is then reused to oxidise triose phosphate, allowing ATP to be synthesised.

Knowledge check 11

Explain what would happen to the production of ATP in an organism if:

a its body temperature rose slightly

b there was a reduced concentration of enzymes in the mitochondrial matrix

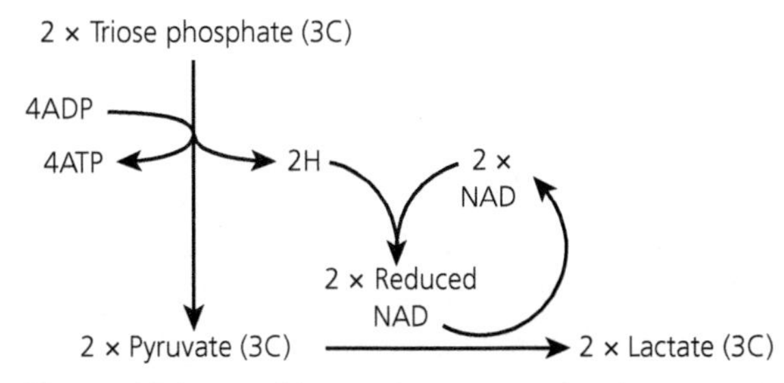

Figure 21 Anaerobic respiration in animals

Figure 22 shows the anaerobic pathway in plants and fungi. Pyruvate undergoes a decarboxylation reaction to produce ethanal and carbon dioxide. The ethanal is then reduced by $NADH_2$ to form ethanol. This recycles NAD, which can then be reused to oxidise triose phosphate.

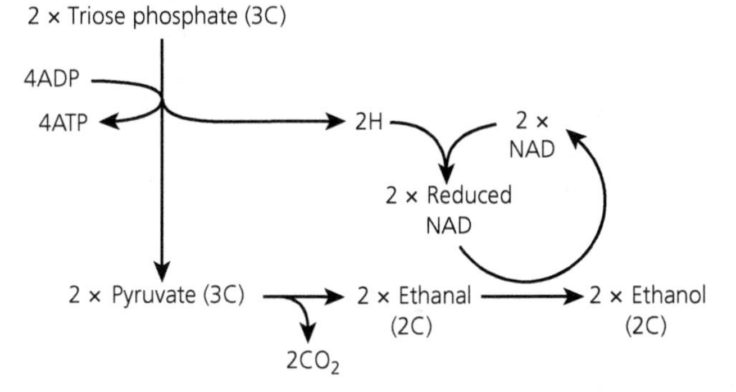

Figure 22 Anaerobic respiration in plants and fungi

Comparison of energy yields

Not all the energy of the glucose molecule is transferred to the ATP. There is a loss of energy as heat energy.

Aerobic respiration involves the complete breakdown of glucose to carbon dioxide and water. It produces 38 *molecules of ATP* per molecule of glucose. It is about 40% efficient.

Anaerobic respiration involves the incomplete breakdown of glucose and produces *two molecules of ATP* per molecule of glucose. It is about 2% efficient. Energy still remains locked up in lactate/ethanol.

Alternative respiratory substrates

Under certain circumstances fats and proteins may be used as respiratory substrates. Individuals are able to survive for long periods without food because they can use their reserves of carbohydrate, fat and protein:

- Glycerol is converted into (3C) triose phosphate, an intermediate in glycolysis.
- Long-chain fatty acid molecules are split into 2C acetate fragments, which enter the Krebs cycle as acetyl coenzyme A.

Knowledge check 12

State the name of the molecule that acts as the terminal electron acceptor in the following:

a aerobic respiration

b anaerobic respiration in a muscle cell

c anaerobic respiration in yeast

Exam tip

Due to factors such as the transport of pyruvate and ADP into the mitochondrial matrix, and leakage of H^+ through the inner mitochondrial membrane, the maximum yield of 38 ATP molecules is not achieved. Current estimates are between 30 and 32 ATPs per glucose.

- Proteins can also be used as a source of energy. If a person eats a high-protein diet excess amino acids are metabolised in the liver. If a person is starving tissue protein is hydrolysed into its constituent amino acids. These amino acids are deaminated, forming ammonia and a keto-acid. Some keto-acids enter glycolysis (e.g. pyruvate) while others enter the Krebs cycle.

Practical work

Factors that affect the rate of respiration

Like photosynthesis, the rate of respiration can be affected by both internal and external factors. Internal factors include the type and concentration of respiratory substrate as well as the concentration of respiratory enzymes. External factors include the concentration of oxygen, temperature and pH. This provides examiners with opportunities to assess a range of practical and mathematical skills, which could include:

- the identification of controlled variables
- drawing graphs and calculations of rates

You may be provided with a method that a student used to obtain their data. You could be asked to identify any limitations in the method that may have led to inaccurate results and how the method could therefore be improved. These limitations could be due to the internal factors that are beyond your control, and therefore you can only attempt to minimise them.

It might be difficult to improve the accuracy of the data, but by carrying out more repeats the reliability of the mean data will be increased.

To investigate the factors affecting the rate of respiration any organism could potentially be used. However, by using a unicellular organism, such as yeast, the majority of variables can be controlled. For example, the effect of temperature could be investigated by adding a fixed mass of a known substrate (e.g. glucose) to a fixed volume of yeast suspension.

The rate of respiration can be interpreted by recording the colour change of an artificial hydrogen acceptor, such as methylene blue or DCPIP. Both of these indicators are blue when oxidised but colourless when reduced.

During respiration, dehydrogenase enzymes catalyse the removal of pairs of hydrogen atoms from intermediate molecules, such as pyruvate. These hydrogen atoms then combine with the coenzymes NAD (and FAD), reducing them. However, these hydrogen atoms will also reduce the indicators, turning them colourless.

Exam tip

As respiration is a series of enzyme-catalysed reactions, any factor that affects enzymes, such as temperature or pH, will affect the rate of respiration.

Summary

After studying this topic you should be able to demonstrate and apply your knowledge and understanding of:

- the role of respiration in providing energy in the cells of all living organisms
- the process of glycolysis in the production of pyruvate, ATP and $NADH_2$
- the formation of acetyl CoA during the link reaction
- the Krebs cycle in the production of ATP, $NADH_2$ and $FADH_2$, with the release of carbon dioxide
- the role of $NADH_2$ and $FADH_2$ as a source of electrons and protons for the electron transport system
- the terms dehydrogenation, decarboxylation, substrate-level phosphorylation and oxidative phosphorylation
- the synthesis of ATP by means of a flow of protons through the enzyme ATP synthase by chemiosmosis
- the breakdown of glucose under anaerobic conditions
- the comparative efficiency of ATP production under aerobic and anaerobic conditions
- the potential use of all organic molecules as respiratory substrates and how lipids and amino acid are utilised

Microbiology

Microbiology is the study of organisms that are too small to be seen with the naked eye.

For thousands of years people have been manipulating microorganisms to produce various foods and drinks, including bread, cheese, yoghurt, beer and wine. With increased knowledge and understanding of microorganisms, modern biotechnology is used to produce other useful products, such as enzymes and antibiotics.

Genetic engineering has offered the potential to produce a wide range of products including human proteins such as insulin. To produce useful products such as new antibiotics it is necessary to:

- be able to culture microorganisms in the laboratory
- have an understanding of a microorganism's metabolism to provide the optimum conditions for growth and the production of the useful product

Bacterial classification

Bacteria are classified by the shape of their cells and their reaction to the Gram stain, both of which are due to the structure of their cell walls.

There are two types of bacterial cell wall (Figure 23):

- **Gram-positive** bacteria have a thick layer consisting of peptidoglycan.
- **Gram-negative** bacteria have a thin layer consisting of peptidoglycan covered by a layer containing lipopolysaccharides.

The layer of lipopolysaccharides provides some protection against antibiotics and the enzyme lysozyme, making Gram-negative bacteria more difficult to kill.

Exam tip

Synoptic link to cell structure: Look back at your notes from A-level year 1 and construct a table comparing the structure of a prokaryotic cell with that of a eukaryotic cell.

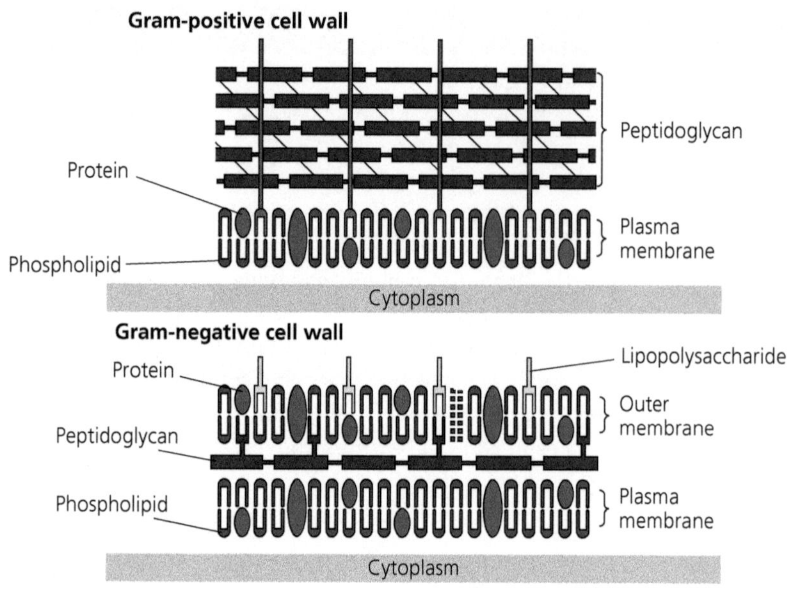

Figure 23 The difference in structure of the cell wall in Gram-positive and Gram-negative bacteria

Classification by shape

There are three main types of bacteria as classified by shape (Figure 24). The shape of the bacteria is due to their rigid cell wall, which has a unique structure.

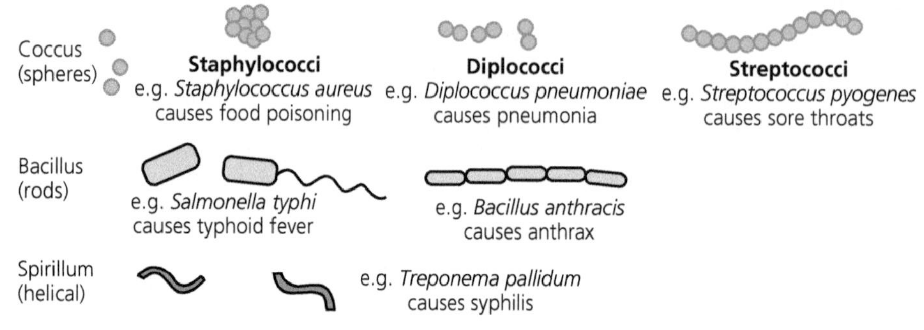

Figure 24 The classification of bacteria by shape

Classification by reaction to the Gram stain

Different types of bacteria can also be identified using the **Gram stain**. The Gram stain procedure and the colours that the bacteria are stained are shown in Figure 25.

- **Gram-positive** bacteria stain purple because their cell walls retain crystal violet.
- **Gram-negative** bacteria are stained red by the counterstain, as their cell walls do not retain crystal violet.

The Gram reaction reflects the more complex structure of Gram-negative cell walls. When treated with acetone, the Gram-negative cell walls lose their outer lipopolysaccharide membrane. This washes the crystal violet stain from the cell, exposing the inner peptidoglycan layer, which stains red with safranin.

Knowledge check 13

Staphylococcus aureus is a Gram-positive bacterium. Describe the shape of its cell and the structure of its cell wall.

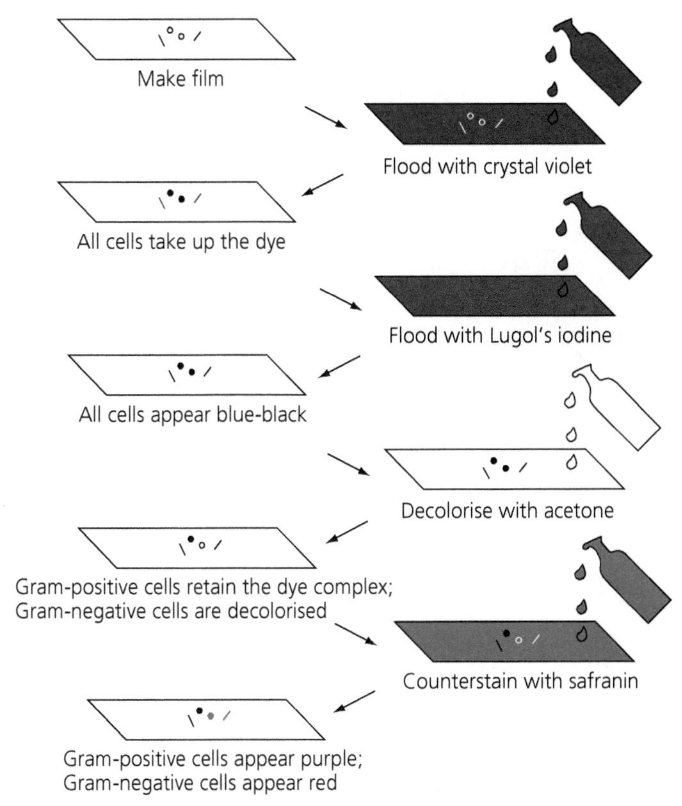

Figure 25 The stages involved in the Gram staining technique

Exam tip

When asked to explain the results produced from the Gram staining technique a common error is to state that Gram-positive bacteria stain purple while Gram-negative do not. Both types stain purple, however the Gram-positive bacteria retain the crystal violet stain whereas the Gram-negative bacteria do not.

Culturing bacteria

To study individual species of bacteria they have to be isolated and cultured. Bacterial cultures must be handled in such a way as to prevent their contamination by unwanted organisms. Of equal importance is the need to ensure that no organisms escape to cause damage to health and the environment.

Aseptic techniques aim to prevent contamination of cultures and the environment. Figure 26 shows the aseptic techniques involved in the transfer of bacteria from a culture bottle to an agar plate.

Aseptic techniques

Before culturing bacteria the equipment and media must be sterilised. Heat is normally used, with the equipment being placed in an autoclave at 121°C for 15 minutes.

1 Hands must be washed (before and after) with antibacterial soap.
2 The work surface must be cleaned (before and after) with disinfectant.
3 A sterile Petri dish containing sterile agar jelly is used. (Heat-labile plastics are irradiated.)
4 The plate is inoculated close to a Bunsen burner. This provides updrafts that move airborne microorganisms away from the plates.

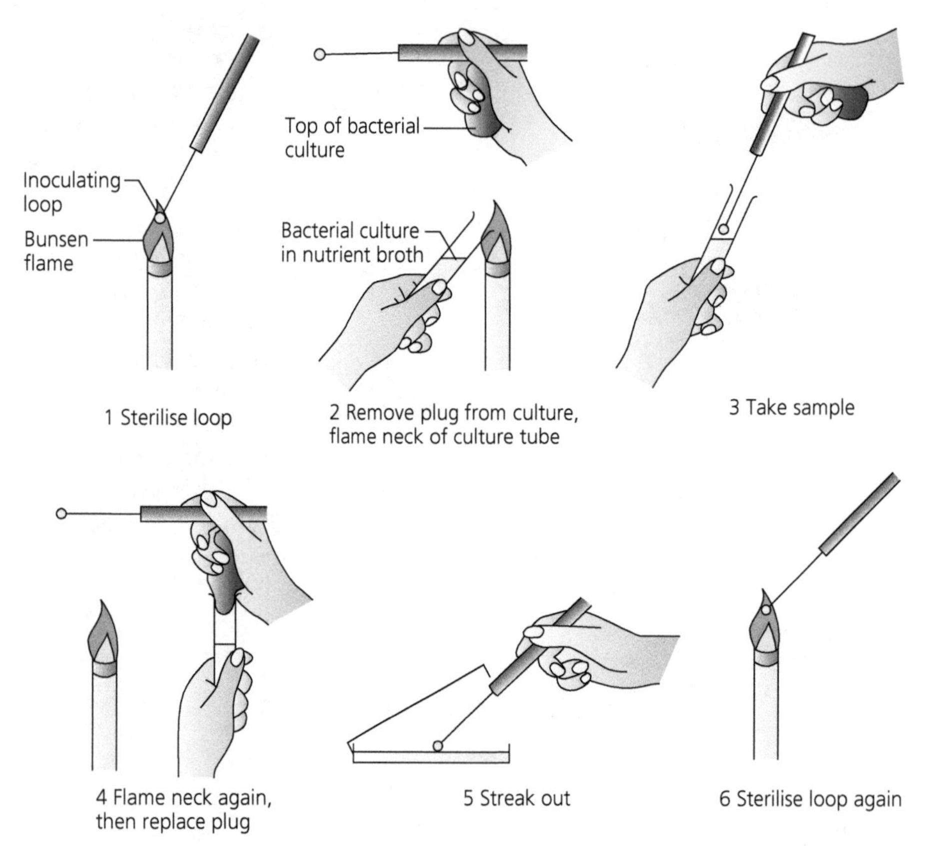

Figure 26 Aseptic techniques and the safe transfer of microorganisms

5 The lid of the culture bottle is removed and kept in the hand, away from the surface of the bench. The mouth of the culture bottle is flamed to kill any unwanted microbes.
6 A flamed inoculating loop or sterile pipette is used to transfer the bacterial culture to the agar plate.
7 When inoculating the plate, the lid of the Petri dish is opened only just wide enough to add the sample.
8 The plates are then secured with adhesive tape and incubated.

Exam tip

Human pathogenic bacteria grow best under anaerobic conditions at 37°C. It is therefore important not to completely seal the inoculated plates with adhesive tape and to incubate the plates at a lower temperature, usually 25°C.

Factors affecting growth

Each species has its **optimum conditions** for growth.

Nutrients

The nutrient broth or agar provided must contain certain nutrients to allow population growth. Microorganisms require:

- a source of carbon, nitrogen and phosphorus
- a respiratory substrate, which is normally glucose
- vitamins and minerals to act as coenzymes
- water — all metabolic reactions occur in aqueous solution

If a nutrient is depleted it will be a limiting factor and reduce the growth rate.

Temperature

Growth is coordinated by enzymes. Enzymes work most efficiently over a narrow range of temperatures (around the optimum). If the temperature falls too low, the rate of enzyme-catalysed reactions becomes too low to sustain life. If the temperature is too high, the denaturation of enzymes causes cell death.

The optimum range of temperature for most microorganisms is between 20°C and 45°C. These bacteria are called mesophiles. Thermophiles have an optimum temperature range above 45°C. Psychrophiles have an optimum temperature range below 20°C.

pH

Bacterial enzymes only work efficiently within a narrow range of pH. For most species this is between pH 5 and pH 7.5 (this is why stomach acid kills most species of bacteria). However, microorganisms in general can tolerate a wider range of pH than plant and animal cells. Some species grow in very acidic environments (pH 2.5); others grow in very alkaline conditions (pH 9).

Oxygen

Different microorganisms have different oxygen requirements:

- Microorganisms that require oxygen for metabolism at all times are called **obligate aerobes**.
- Some microorganisms find oxygen toxic as it inhibits their respiration and they cannot grow in its presence. These are called **obligate anaerobes**.
- Populations of some bacteria grow rapidly in the presence of oxygen, but can survive without it, although their population growth rate is slow. These are called **facultative anaerobes**.

Practical work

Investigating the numbers of bacteria in fresh and stale milk

The culturing of microorganisms provides examiners with excellent opportunities to assess your mathematical skills as well as your understanding of aseptic technique.

A number of techniques can be used to estimate population. There are two types of population estimate:

- A **total count** includes both living and dead cells. It can be measured by haemocytometry. A disadvantage of this type of count is that the numbers in the population can be overestimated, due to the inclusion of dead cells.
- A **viable count** includes only living cells. This technique involves growing bacteria to form distinct colonies that can be counted. It is based on the assumption that a single cell gives rise to a single colony. A disadvantage of this technique is that numbers can be underestimated because of clumping of cells when the plates are made, i.e. several cells forming a single colony.

Pure cultures of microorganisms contain too many cells to allow an accurate count to be made. Therefore the original culture is diluted down, usually in ten-fold steps, to provide a final number within a countable range. This is known as **serial dilution** (Figure 27).

→

Knowledge check 14

Explain why bacteria require a source of carbon, nitrogen and phosphorus.

Knowledge check 15

The bacterium *Escherichia coli* is a Gram-negative facultative anaerobe. Describe what is meant by the terms 'Gram-negative' and 'facultative anaerobe'.

Knowledge check 16

Use the agar plate labelled E in Figure 27 to estimate the number of bacteria in 1 cm^3 of the original culture.

Steps involved in a serial dilution

1. 1 cm^3 of the original culture is transferred into 9 cm^3 of sterile nutrient medium (or sterile water). This is then mixed to ensure an even distribution (10^{-1} dilution).
2. 1 cm^3 of this mixture is transferred into 9 cm^3 of sterile nutrient medium and mixed (10^{-2} dilution).
3. The process is then repeated a number of times to produce further 10-fold dilutions. In order to carry out a viable count a known volume of each bacterial culture, usually 1 cm^3 or 0.1 cm^3, is added to agar plates and incubated.

Aseptic technique is required throughout.

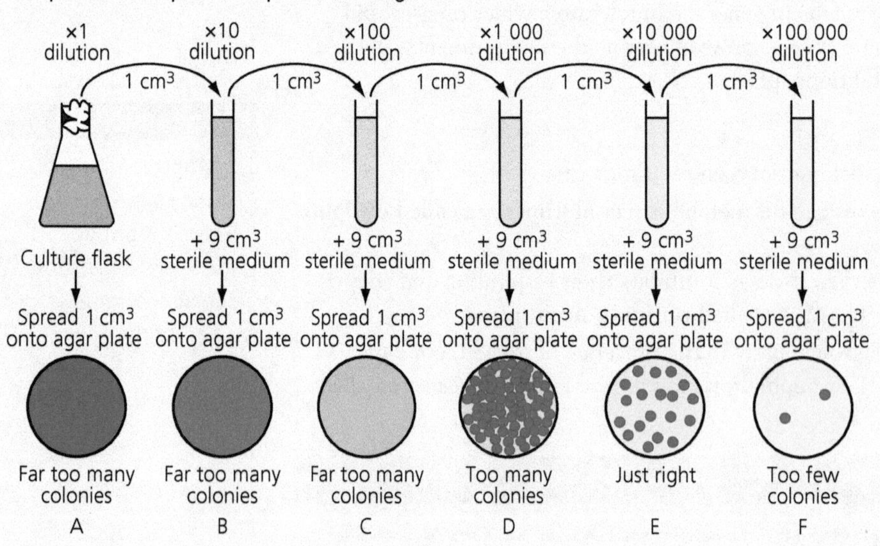

Figure 27 The steps involved in dilution plating

It can be seen from Figure 27 that some plates have far too many colonies, many of which have merged, meaning that it is impossible to count individual colonies. Other plates have only a few colonies, so they cannot be representative of the original culture.

To calculate the total viable cell count in the original culture, the number of colonies present is multiplied by the dilution factor.

Exam tip

Sometimes serial dilutions involve the transfer of 1 cm^3 of the culture into 99 cm^3 of sterile nutrient medium. This produces a 10^{-2} dilution. If 1 cm^3 of this dilution is transferred to 99 cm^3 of sterile nutrient medium it will produce a 10^{-4} dilution. If asked on the exam to calculate the numbers of bacteria in the original sample make sure that you read the information carefully: is it a 1-in-10 or a 1-in-100 dilution and is 1 cm^3 or 0.1 cm^3 of the dilution being used to plate out?

Knowledge check 17

What is the difference between a total count and a viable count? Explain how these methods can overestimate or underestimate the size of a bacterial population.

Summary

After studying this topic you should be able to demonstrate and apply your knowledge and understanding of:

- the classification of bacteria according to their shape and by their reaction to the Gram stain
- how microorganisms can be cultured in the laboratory and the principles of aseptic techniques
- the requirements for growth of microorganisms in relation to temperature, pH, nutrients and oxygen
- the difference between a total count and a viable count when monitoring population growth
- how a viable count is carried out, using serial dilutions, plating and counting of colonies

Population size and ecosystems

Ecological definitions

Ecosystem: a community of living organisms (biotic component) and the abiotic factors that influence them.

Population: a group of interbreeding individuals of the same species, found in a particular habitat, at a particular time.

Community: all of the populations of different species living in a particular habitat at a particular time.

Habitat: the physical environment where a particular population or community is found.

Environment: the set of external conditions (biotic and abiotic) that surround an organism:

- **biotic factors** — living component, i.e. the community
- **abiotic factors** — non-living component, for example temperature

Ecological niche: the place where an organism is found and what it does there, i.e. its role in the ecosystem. It is determined by its adaptations to food and the abiotic factors that are present.

Exam tip

Ecosystems vary in size from the very small to the very large. When thinking about ecosystems, ponds and rock-pools make excellent examples. They are something that you will have experience of, and you will be able to list many of the biotic and abiotic components within them.

Exam tip

Due to interspecific competition only one species can occupy a niche in a particular habitat. This is known as the competitive exclusion principle.

Populations

Populations are dynamic, constantly changing components of ecosystems. When a species successfully invades a new area and establishes itself, the growth of its population follows a predictable pattern. The maximum population size that a particular environment can support indefinitely is called the **carrying capacity**.

A **population** is defined as a group of interbreeding individuals of the same species in a particular habitat at a particular time. Figure 28 shows that the size of a population is determined by four factors:

- **Births** and **immigration** increase population size.
- **Deaths** and **emigration** decrease population size.

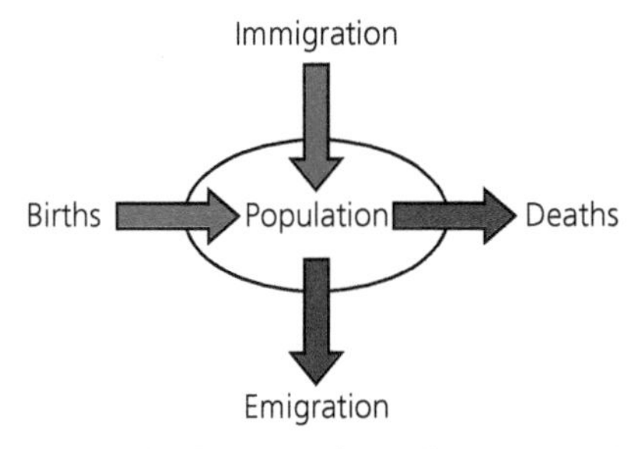

Figure 28 Factors that affect a population

Population growth

population growth = (births + immigration) – (deaths + emigration)

Due to migration it can be difficult to measure population growth accurately. However, microorganisms can be cultured in the laboratory and provide a simplistic but useful model for population growth.

Population growth in the laboratory

When microorganisms, such as yeast, are grown under laboratory conditions there are four phases of population growth (Figure 29).

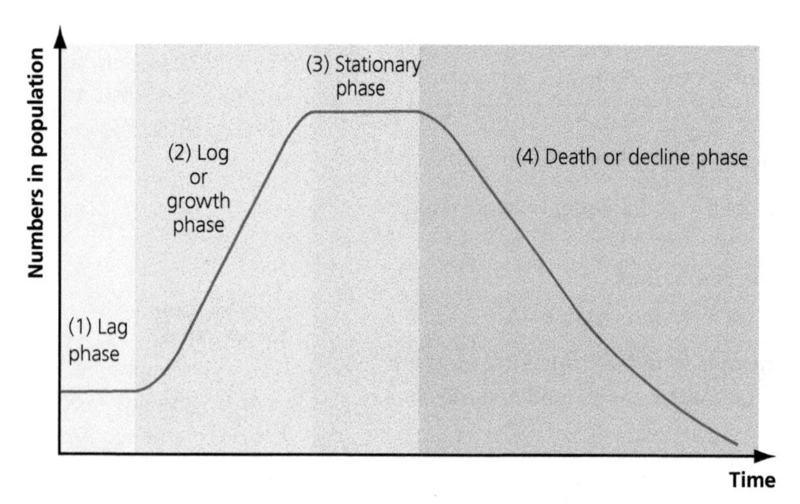

Figure 29 The population growth curve of a bacterial culture grown under laboratory conditions

During the **lag phase** there is a slow increase in the number of cells in the population. The yeast cells are adjusting to their new environment. This involves switching on genes and producing digestive enzymes. As yeast cells are saprophytic they secrete these enzymes and digest the medium extracellularly. The soluble products of digestion are then absorbed.

During the **log phase** nutrients are in plentiful supply and the waste products (ethanol) that have been produced are in low concentrations. The rate of cell division is at a maximum and the population is undergoing **exponential growth**.

During the **stationary phase** the **carrying capacity** (maximum population size that the environment can support indefinitely) has been reached and equilibrium is established. The number of new cells being added to the population is *equal* to the number of cells dying. **Limiting factors** (nutrient depletion and waste accumulation) prevent a further increase in population size.

During the **death** or **decline phase**, more cells are dying than are being produced. This is because of shortage of nutrients and/or the accumulation of waste (ethanol). The population begins to decrease.

Exam tip

When answering questions about the phases of the growth curve avoid making vague statements and give a detailed answer demonstrating your understanding of biology. You must be careful not to refer to 'birth rate' when talking about yeast, as this will not gain credit.

Exponential growth When the number of individuals in the population doubles per unit time.

Population growth in the natural environment

In the natural environment, when a species successfully invades and establishes itself in a new area, the growth of its population shows the following pattern:

- a period of slow growth, i.e. a lag phase
- a period of rapid population growth, i.e. a log phase
- a period of equilibrium when its numbers remain more or less constant, i.e. a stationary phase (Figure 30)

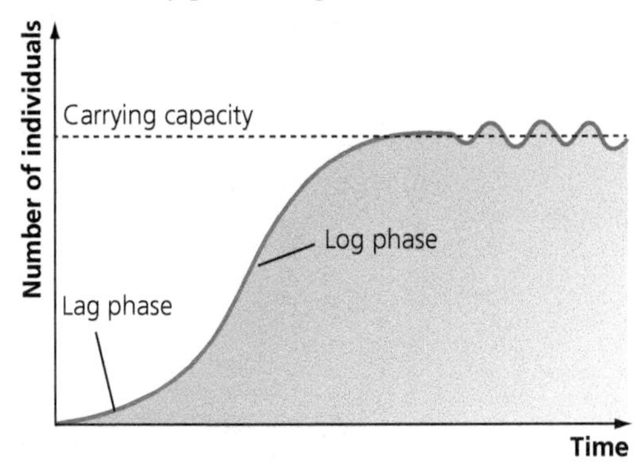

Figure 30 Population growth under 'natural' conditions

During the lag phase the increase in population is slow. There is a limited number of individuals of reproductive age in the population.

In the log phase there is a plentiful supply of nutrients. There is little intraspecific competition for nutrients and resources. The waste products that have been produced are in low concentrations. The birth rate is at a maximum and population growth is exponential.

Knowledge check 18

Explain what causes the lag phase in a species that reproduces sexually (e.g. rats) and in yeast (which reproduces asexually).

Limits to population growth

As the population nears the carrying capacity of the environment the growth rate slows down. This is known as environmental resistance and several factors will limit further population growth. These factors can be either density dependent or density independent.

Knowledge check 19

Explain what is meant by the following terms:

a carrying capacity
b exponential growth

Density-dependent factors

The effect of a density-dependent factor increases as the density of the population increases, i.e. a greater percentage of the population is affected at higher population densities. Density-dependent factors include the availability of food, competition, predation and disease.

For example, it is much easier for pathogens such as the influenza virus to spread from one animal to another at higher population densities. Therefore a higher percentage of people within a population will have influenza as the population density increases. (This explains why influenza is more common in the winter as people become crowded indoors.) In this way density-dependent factors slow down the population growth rate.

Most natural populations tend to fluctuate around the carrying capacity (i.e. a stationary/stable phase). The carrying capacity is dependent on the availability of resources, for example the concentration of nutrients such as nitrates. If the population rises above the carrying capacity then there will be increased competition for nitrates. This will increase the death rate and/or decrease the birth rate — the death rate will exceed the birth rate and the population will decrease. If the population falls below the carrying capacity then there will be decreased competition for nitrates. The birth rate will exceed the death rate and the population will increase.

Density-independent factors

The effect of a density-independent factor is the same regardless of the size of the population, i.e. the same percentage of the population is affected, irrespective of the population density. Density-independent factors include the weather and climate, for example a sudden change in temperature.

Take small birds such as wrens as an example. They are susceptible to low temperatures and a sudden freeze may kill a fixed percentage (say 70%) of the birds, irrespective of the population density. Density-independent factors can, therefore, lead to a population crash.

Knowledge check 21

Intraspecific competition for food can act in both a density-dependent manner and a density-independent manner. In an experiment, the number of eggs of the flour beetle added to a fixed volume of flour was varied and the number of beetles dying monitored. Figure 31 shows some of the results. Use the graph to determine the type of competition shown by flour beetles and give a reason for your answer.

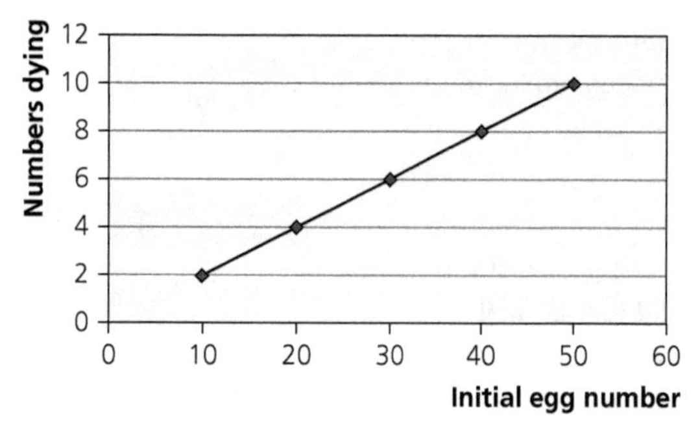

Figure 31 The effect of competition on the survival of flour beetles

Exam tip

When asked to define the terms density-dependent factors and density-independent factors many students get it wrong and make reference to 'the effect of the population on the factor'. This is incorrect — the reference should be to 'the effect of the factor on the population'.

Knowledge check 20

State two density-dependent factors and one density-independent factor that can affect the carrying capacity.

Exam tip

Exam questions on this topic are usually about a specific organism and you might not gain credit for using vague terms such as food, resources or nutrients. Try to be specific with your answers. For example, carrot plants growing in a field will be competing with one another for light, water and nitrates; male tigers will be competing with each other for territories and females.

Investigating competition

Organisms compete with each other for limited resources, such as food, water, nesting sites or territories, and mates.

- **Intraspecific competition** is between individuals of the same species, for example carrot plants competing for water and nitrates.
- **Interspecific competition** is between individuals of different species, for example carrot plants competing for water and nitrates with weeds such as dandelions.

The population growth of unicellular organisms, such as *Paramecium*, can be monitored within the laboratory. They are grown in tubes of liquid medium that contains yeast cells. *P. caudatum* and *P. aurelia* feed on yeast cells suspended in the medium; *P. bursaria* feeds on yeast cells at the bottom of the tubes. When the different species are grown separately each reaches a maximum population size (Figure 32). →

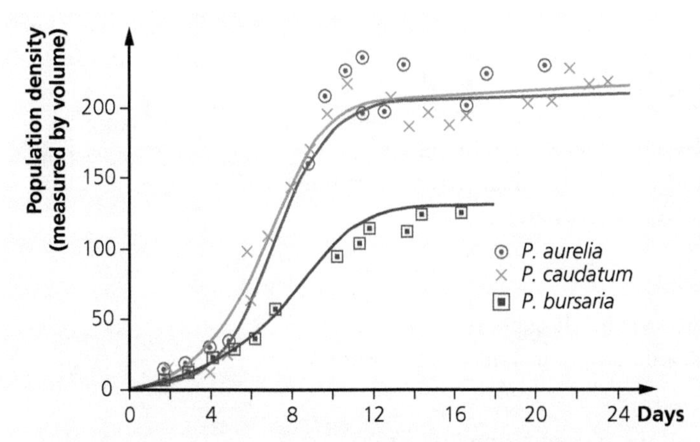

Figure 32 Population growth in three species of *Paramecium* grown in isolation

Figure 33a shows that when *P. caudatum* and *P. aurelia* are grown together only one species reaches its carrying capacity. The other population declines and eventually dies out. This is because they are in direct competition and *P. aurelia* outcompetes *P. caudatum*, which becomes locally extinct. This is an example of the competitive exclusion principle.

Figure 33b shows that when *P. caudatum* and *P. bursaria* are grown together, the species coexist, but with smaller populations than when grown alone. They are able to coexist because they feed in different areas. Their maximum populations are smaller because they are competing for the same food source.

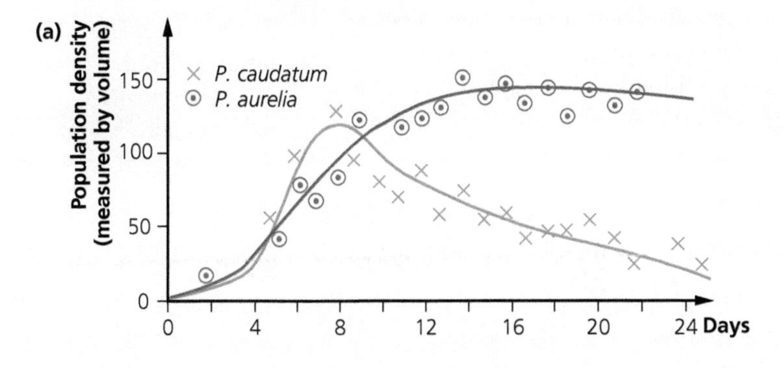

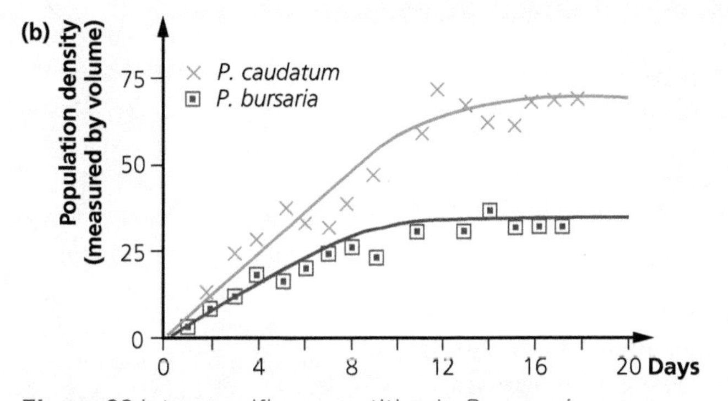

Figure 33 Interspecific competition in *Paramecium*

Knowledge check 22

Explain why the introduction of grey squirrels into the British Isles has led to a decline in the number of native red squirrels.

Succession

Ecosystems are **dynamic** and are constantly changing. This can be brought about by changes in the physical environment (abiotic factors), for example nitrate concentration, and by the activities of organisms within the community (biotic factors), for example taller plants shading shorter plants. The gradual change from one community type to another is referred to as **ecological succession**.

Ecological succession The change in the *structure* and *species composition* of a community over *time*.

Primary succession

Primary succession occurs in a habitat that had not previously supported a community, for example bare rock following a volcanic eruption. This can be a very slow process as soil formation has to occur.

The first species to colonise the new area are called the **pioneer species**. These species, such as lichens, are well adapted to be able to survive, and reproduce, in these harsh environments. Lichens also secrete acid to extract minerals from the rock. This starts to erode the rock and begins the process of soil formation.

Once pioneer species become established, they will stabilise the substrate and *change the abiotic conditions*. For example, when they die they will add organic matter (humus) to the soil. Upon decomposition they will also provide nutrients, such as nitrates, allowing other species to colonise. Due to the change in abiotic conditions, the new species have advantages that allow them to **outcompete** the pioneer species. They may grow larger leaves and so can absorb more sunlight energy.

Exam tip

This is a good example of interspecific competition between plants of different species competing for the same resources, such as nitrates.

This process continues because as one community of organisms changes the abiotic environment, new species will migrate into the area and outcompete those species, allowing a different community to take over. In natural conditions succession progresses through various **seral stages** before reaching a climax community. Climax communities, for example woodland, change very little over time; they are the final stage in ecological succession (Figure 34).

Seral stages The different stages in succession when particular communities dominate, e.g. grasses.

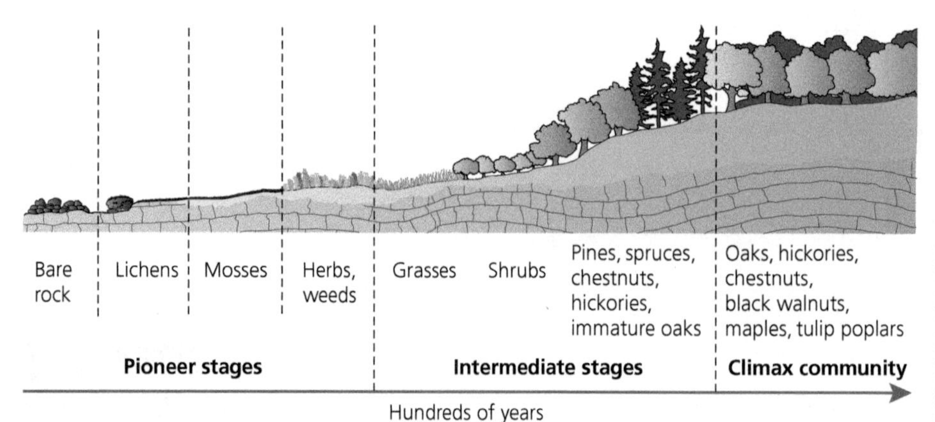

Figure 34 An example of ecological succession

Ecological succession leads to an increase in the **species diversity** of ecosystems through an increasing number of available niches. As succession progresses, communities contain a greater number of plant species. These will provide a greater number of niches, leading to an increased number of animal species present.

Exam tip

When answering questions linking succession with species diversity you must refer to *species* in your answer. It is not simply that 'more plants allow more animals to be present'. It is the increase in number of *species* of plants that provides the niches to allow an increased number of *species* of animals.

As species diversity increases so does the stability of the ecosystem. Pioneer communities have low species diversity and are therefore unstable and subject to change. Climax communities have high species diversity and are relatively stable.

Secondary succession

Secondary succession occurs when species recolonise a habitat, i.e. where there had previously been a community, for example following deforestation. This is a much more rapid process than primary succession because soil, containing seeds, is already present.

Energy transfer through ecosystems

Some ecosystems, such as those based around deep-sea hydrothermal vents, obtain their energy from chemical reactions. However, the majority of organisms on the planet obtain their energy either directly, or indirectly, from the Sun. **Producers** are organisms that can directly utilise light energy, for example plants, whereas **consumers** can only utilise energy contained within organic molecules synthesised by the producers, or other consumers.

Primary productivity

Plants and algae are examples of photoautotrophs. During photosynthesis, they convert simple inorganic molecules (CO_2 and H_2O) into complex organic molecules (triose phosphate) using light energy. They therefore convert light energy into chemical energy within the bonds of the organic molecules.

The majority of light falling on a plant is not incorporated into plant tissue:

- Some light will be *reflected* from the plant surface.
- Some light fails to strike a chlorophyll molecule and is *transmitted* through the leaf.
- Some light is of the *wrong wavelength* for photosynthesis.

The rate of production of chemical energy in organic molecules, during photosynthesis, is known as **gross primary productivity** (**GPP**). In order grow the plant must produce new cells, which requires energy. Therefore, some of these organic molecules are respired to provide the ATP required for growth. The rate at which organic molecules are stored as new cells/tissue is known as **net primary productivity** (**NPP**).

NPP = GPP – energy lost during respiration

GPP and NPP are measured in $kJ\,m^{-2}y^{-1}$. Net primary productivity results in an increase in plant biomass; this biomass is available to the primary consumers (herbivores).

Secondary productivity

The rate at which energy from one trophic level is used to make new animal cells/tissue is called secondary production. The efficiency of energy transfer between trophic levels varies from ecosystem to ecosystem. The transfer of chemical energy, contained within biomass, occurs through food chains. However, it is very inefficient — approximately 10% of the energy passes between each trophic level. Three main factors contribute to this 90% loss of energy:

- Parts of the organism are *not eaten*, for example woody material or bones and shells.

Exam tip

Synoptic link to photosynthesis: Factors such as CO_2 concentration can also limit the rate of photosynthesis.

Exam tip

Synoptic link to respiration: During respiration, only some of the energy released from the oxidation of organic molecules is used to synthesise ATP. The rest is converted to heat energy and lost to the environment.

- Parts of the organism that are eaten are *not digested*, for example cellulose, and pass out in faeces.
- During cellular respiration energy is lost as *heat* energy to the surroundings.

It is very rare to find food chains with more than five trophic levels. The loss of energy, at each stage, limits the length and there is not enough energy available to support another **population** of consumers.

The energy contained within the uneaten tissues and indigestible molecules is then transferred to the **decomposers** — saprophytic bacteria and fungi. In order to reproduce and make new cells, the decomposers must respire some of the organic molecules they absorb. Ultimately all of the energy that enters the food chain, as light energy, is lost from the food chain as heat energy (Figure 35).

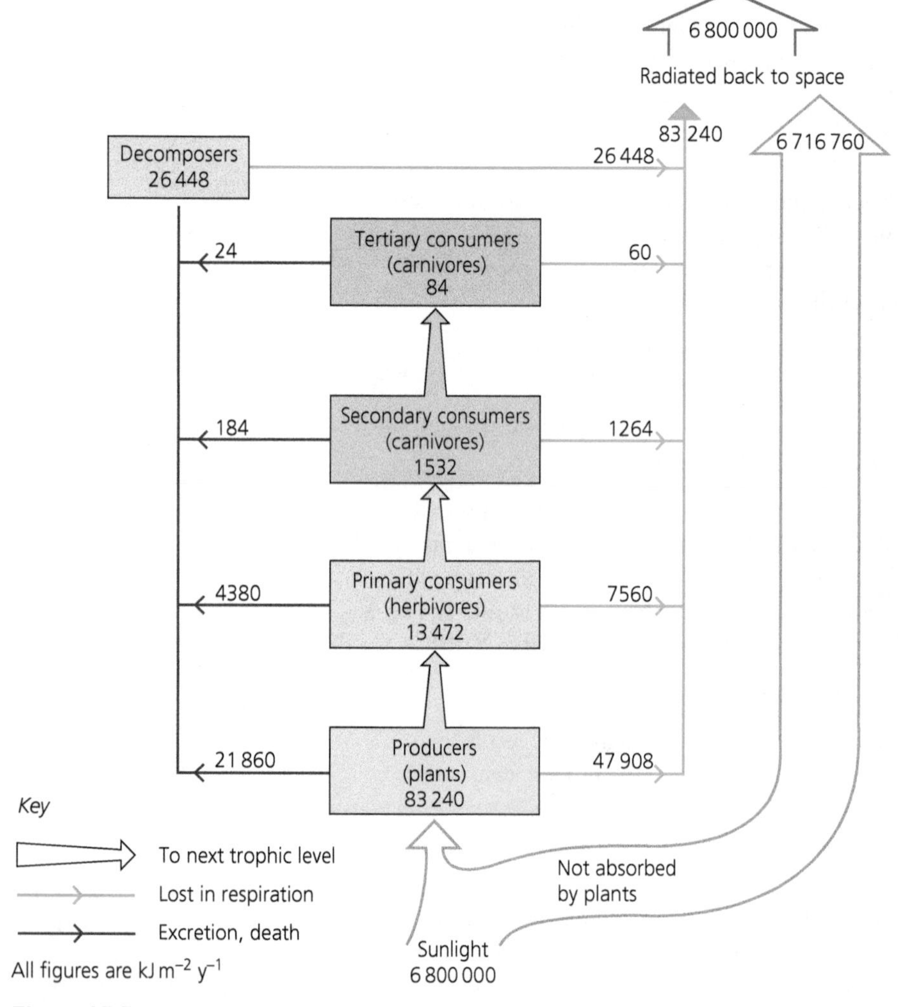

Figure 35 Energy flow through an ecosystem

Exam tip

Some energy is also lost during excretion, as urea is an energy-containing organic molecule. However, this is a relatively small proportion compared with the other losses.

Knowledge check 23

Use Figure 35 to calculate the percentage efficiency of secondary productivity in the primary consumers.

Knowledge check 24

Use your knowledge of digestion to explain why the secondary productivity of carnivores is more efficient than that of herbivores.

Exam tip

Secondary production in exothermic animals is more efficient than in endothermic animals. This is because an endothermic animal must carry out respiration to release heat energy in order to maintain a constant body temperature. An exothermic animal uses its environment to regulate its body temperature.

Ecological pyramids

Food chains can be represented by ecological pyramids. These can represent either the number of organisms in the food chain or the transfer of biomass or energy through the food chain.

A pyramid of numbers represents the total number of organisms at each trophic level in a food chain, at a given point in time. Pyramids of number are simplistic and may be inverted, particularly if the producer is larger than the primary consumer or many parasites feed on consumers (Figure 36).

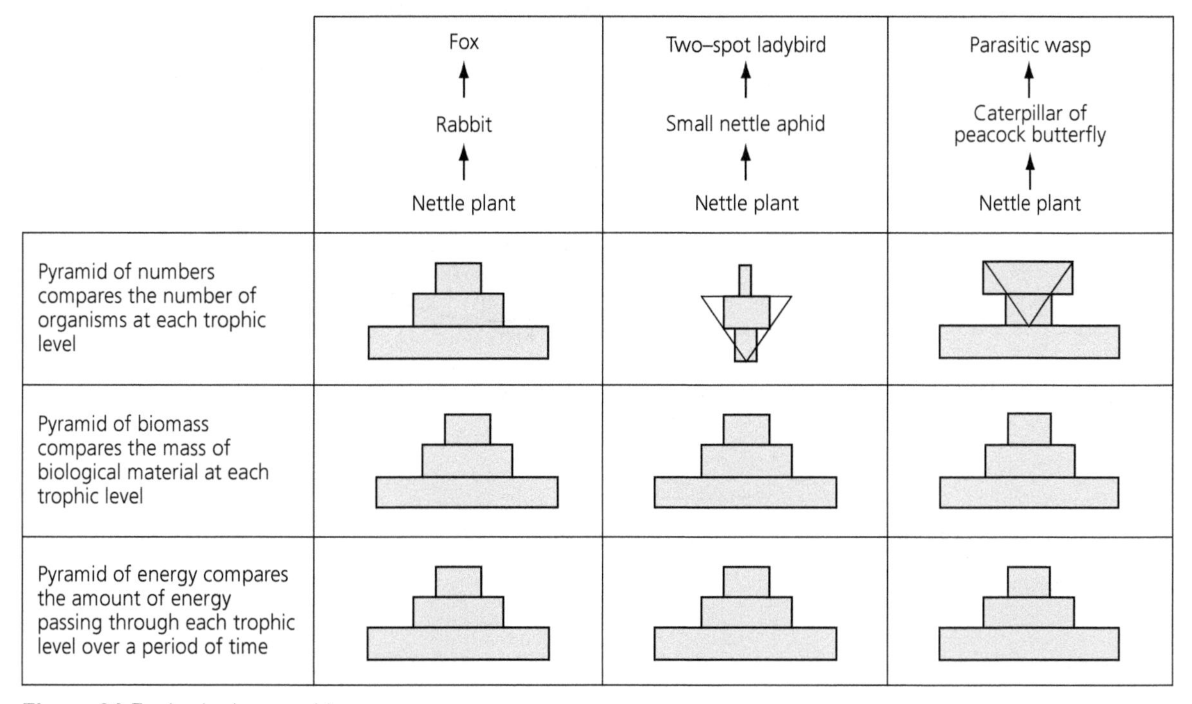

Figure 36 Ecological pyramids

A pyramid of biomass can be constructed by counting the number of individuals present (at each trophic level) in a given area and multiplying it by the average mass of these individuals. The biomass values are expressed in $kg\,m^{-2}$.

Exam tip

In intensive farming practices animals are kept indoors in high densities under temperature-controlled conditions. This increases the efficiency of meat production (secondary productivity) as it reduces respiratory losses due to movement and regulation of body temperature.

Knowledge check 25

The majority of animals reared for food are herbivores and not carnivores. If secondary production is approximately 10% efficient, what mass of plant material would be required to produce:

a 1 kg of herbivore?

b 1 kg of carnivore?

c Use your answers to **a** and **b** to explain why carnivorous animals are not reared for food.

A pyramid of biomass illustrates a sampling situation at a given point in time, and does not represent *productivity*, which is the capacity of any trophic level to produce biomass over a period of time. An inverted pyramid of biomass can occur if the producer level includes small organisms with a rapid rate of reproduction (e.g. phytoplankton) so that they have high productivity over a period of time.

Pyramids of energy represent the flow of energy through each trophic level in an ecosystem during a fixed period of time. The energy values are expressed in $kJ\,m^{-2}y^{-1}$. Pyramids of energy allow comparisons between the productivities of the trophic levels, because a time period is involved. Pyramids of energy are never inverted.

Nutrient cycles

All matter is **recycled** within ecosystems and decomposers play a crucial role. When organisms die, decomposers (fungi and bacteria) break the tissues down. The organic molecules in the tissues are broken down and the inorganic molecules are released into the environment. This enables nutrients to be recycled within ecosystems.

Figure 37 shows a basic nutrient cycle, with the three major feeding groups in an ecosystem (producers, consumers and decomposers) forming a triangle.

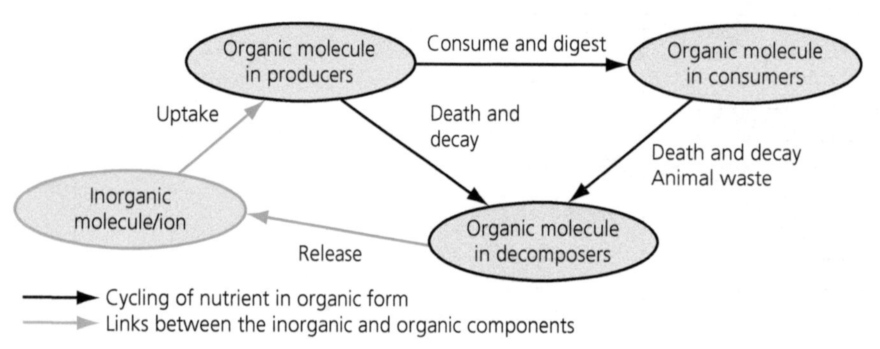

Figure 37 A simple nutrient cycle

Exam tip

Consumers do more than just feed on other organisms. Once the organism is eaten the large insoluble molecules they contain have to be digested. The small soluble products are then absorbed and used to synthesise their own organic molecules (this is known as assimilation).

The carbon cycle

Figure 38 shows a simple carbon cycle:

- Carbon is found in living organisms in carbohydrates, lipids, proteins and nucleic acids.
- The carbon in the atmosphere and oceans is made available to organisms via photosynthesis. Green plants and algae fix carbon dioxide and convert it into complex organic molecules, such as glucose.
- Carbon dioxide is produced by all organisms during respiration and enters the atmosphere.

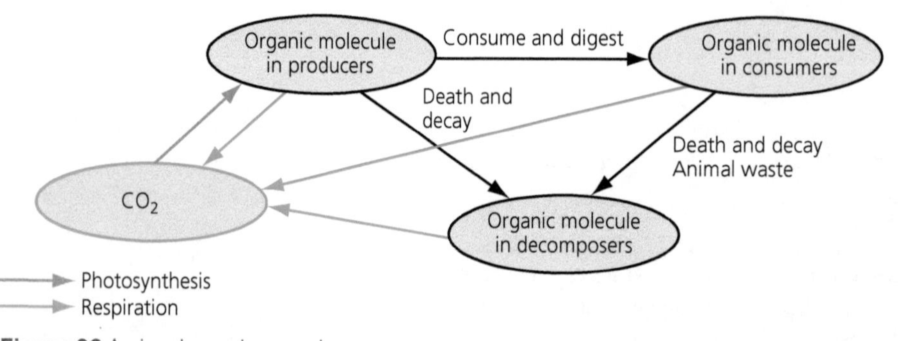

Figure 38 A simple carbon cycle

Human effects on the carbon cycle

Carbon is also stored in wood and fossil fuels (coal, oil and gas). Fossil fuels were formed when plants and animals died and their remains did not decompose but were fossilised. Coal is fossilised wood; oil and gas result from the soft tissues of animals (hard tissues, such as bones, are preserved). The combustion of wood and fossil fuels releases the stored carbon into the atmosphere as carbon dioxide.

Climate change and carbon footprints

Human activities have resulted in an increase in CO_2 in the atmosphere due to:

- **combustion of fossil fuels**, which accounts for 70% of the increase in CO_2
- **deforestation**, which accounts for 30% of the increase in CO_2. With fewer plants less CO_2 is removed from the atmosphere via photosynthesis.

Carbon dioxide is a 'greenhouse gas' as it absorbs radiation from the Earth. This leads to **global warming**, which refers to an average increase in the Earth's temperature. A rise in temperatures will result in altered rainfall patterns, desertification and a rise in sea level. As the climate changes then the distribution of species will be affected and it may lead to the extinction of some species.

As individuals we all contribute to the carbon dioxide emissions that are leading to global warming and climate change. The extent of our contributions can be calculated as a **carbon footprint**. This represents the total amount of carbon dioxide attributable to the actions of an individual or a product or service over a period of 1 year. The carbon footprint is a very powerful tool in understanding the impact of personal behaviour on global warming.

The nitrogen cycle

In living organisms nitrogen is only found in certain molecules — for example, amino acids/proteins and nucleic acids. It is only available to producers as ammonium ions and nitrates in the soil. Nitrogen leaves all organisms after death. It leaves consumers in indigestible matter (faeces) and through nitrogenous excretion (e.g. in urea).

Bacteria are extremely important in the nitrogen cycle. They are responsible for several processes (Figure 39).

1. **Putrefaction/ammonification** occurs when **saprophytic bacteria** metabolise the nitrogen-containing organic matter in dead organisms, faeces and urine and release ammonium ions.
2. **Nitrification** — under aerobic conditions **nitrifying bacteria** convert:
   - ammonia to nitrites (*Nitrosomonas*)
   - nitrites to nitrates (*Nitrobacter*)

   Nitrates are then taken up from the soil by producers.
3. **Denitrification** — **denitrifying bacteria** (*Pseudomonas*) convert nitrates and ammonium ions into atmospheric nitrogen. This occurs in **anaerobic conditions**, for example in waterlogged soils. Denitrification removes nitrogen from ecosystems.

Exam tip

When answering a question on the nitrogen cycle you must clearly state the form that nitrogen is in at each stage. You are more likely to gain credit for an answer that refers to 'proteins' or 'amino acids' when discussing plants and animals rather than using a generic term such as 'nitrogen-containing compounds'.

Knowledge check 26

State two reasons why plants need to absorb nitrates.

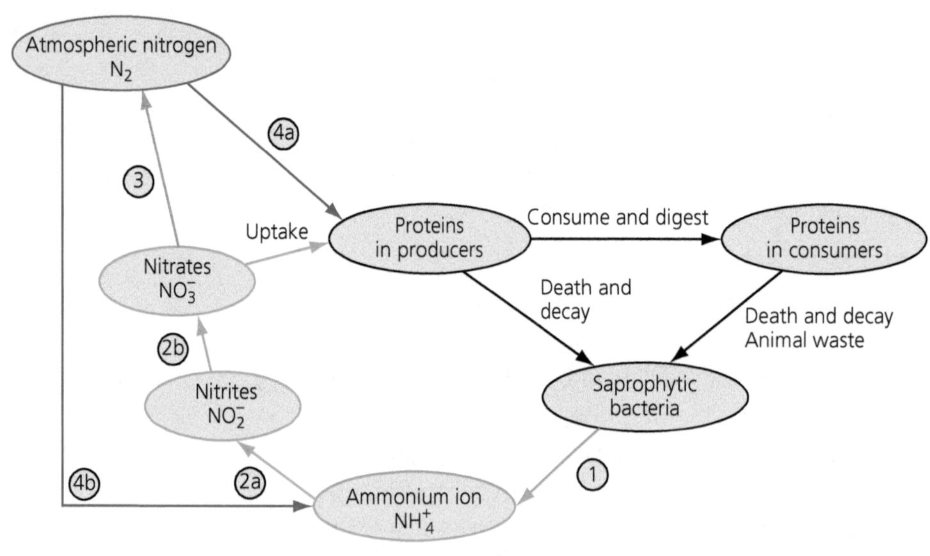

Figure 39 The importance of bacteria in the nitrogen cycle

4 **Nitrogen fixation** — **nitrogen-fixing bacteria** convert atmospheric nitrogen into ammonium ions. Nitrogen fixation is brought about by *Rhizobium* and *Azotobacter*:
   - *Rhizobium* is a genus of mutualistic bacteria found in the root nodules of leguminous plants, such as clover. The plant rapidly converts ammonium ions into nitrogen-containing organic compounds. The bacterium benefits by gaining energy and nutrients, for example carbohydrates, from the plant.
   - *Azotobacter* is found living free in the soil.

Human effects on the nitrogen cycle

The nitrogen cycle is of significant economic importance in relation to human food production. However, when a crop is harvested, the nitrogen-containing organic molecules are removed from the 'ecosystem'. This results in a reduction of organic matter that can be decomposed, which leads to a reduction in the nitrate concentration in the soil.

In order to maintain high yields, farmers must replace the nutrients that have been lost. This can be achieved by applying manure or artificial fertilisers, such as ammonium nitrate, to their fields.

The increased use of artificial fertilisers has had some harmful effects on both terrestrial and aquatic ecosystems:

- It has resulted in reduced species diversity of grasslands, as it encourages the growth of taller plants, such as grasses and nettles, which shade out smaller plants.
- It has caused **eutrophication** of aquatic habitats, leading to a reduction in species diversity (Figure 40).

Exam tip

Although it is unlikely that you would be asked to draw a nitrogen cycle, the ability to do so would help you answer questions based on it. Try to build up a flow in stages.

Stage 1: the 'organic triangle' (in black)

Stage 2: add the inorganic loop (in blue)

Stage 3: add in the names of the processes involved

Stage 4: add the names of the bacteria involved

Stage 5: add atmospheric nitrogen (in red); name the processes involved and the names of the bacteria

Knowledge check 27

Explain how the following farming practices affect the nitrogen cycle:

a draining waterlogged fields
b ploughing fields
c planting leguminous crops such as clover
d ploughing crops, such as clover, into the soil

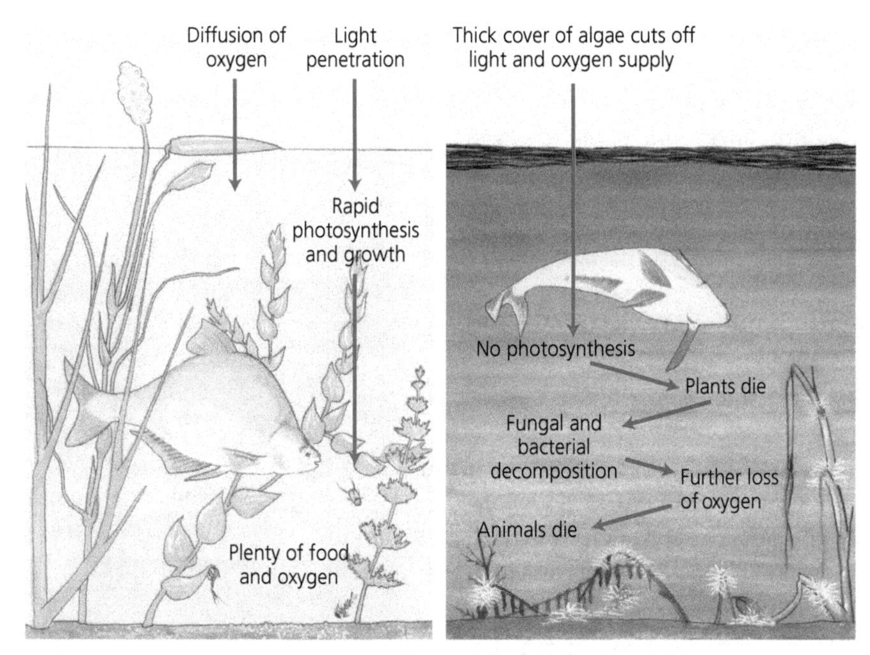

Figure 40 The effects of eutrophication

Eutrophication occurs when nitrates (and phosphates) are leached from the soil and enter rivers and lakes. The increased nitrate concentration results in the rapid growth of algae, resulting in an algal bloom. This prevents light from penetrating into the lake and as a result aquatic plants are unable to photosynthesise and die.

Saprophytic bacteria decompose the dead plants (and dead algae, which are short-lived) and increase in number. Bacterial respiration causes the water to become deoxygenated, resulting in the death of oxygen-sensitive species such as fish and stonefly larvae.

Exam tip

Many students confuse the effects of pesticides and artificial fertilisers. Fertilisers do not directly kill animals, such as fish. Fish die due to a lack of oxygen, as an *indirect* effect of artificial fertilisers entering aquatic habitats.

Knowledge check 28

Explain why the application of manure onto a field is less likely to cause eutrophication.

Practical work

During this topic you should have completed some form of practical activity to investigate the abundance and distribution of organisms in a habitat.

- Abundance refers the number of individuals of a particular species.
- Distribution refers to how widespread they are.

The abundance and distribution of plant species in an ecosystem are much easier to record than those of the animal species present. The nature of any investigation is dependent upon the type of habitat being studied. In a habitat where the abiotic factors are uniform, such as a meadow, then quadrat sampling is used. In a habitat where there is an environmental gradient, such as from a meadow into a wood, transects are used.

If you were assessing the abundance and distribution of plants in a meadow, you would need to include the following steps:

1. Mark out a grid using two tape measures at right angles to each other.
2. Choose pairs of numbers at **random** (e.g. use a random-number table) to generate coordinates.

→

3 Place the quadrat at the point corresponding to the coordinates and record the numbers of each species present within the quadrat.
4 *Repeat* the process at least 10 times, to ensure the sample is large enough to be representative.

For some types of plant, such as grass and moss, it is difficult to count the individuals, so the percentage cover of these species is recorded.

If you were assessing the change in abundance and distribution of plants along an environmental gradient, you would need to include the following steps:

1 Use a tape measure to form a transect along the gradient, for example from a meadow into a wood.
2 a At fixed intervals along the tape the species of plant touching the tape is recorded.
  b A better method involves placing a quadrat at fixed intervals along the tape and recording the numbers of each species present within the quadrat. This is known as a belt transect.
3 The abiotic factor that changes along the gradient, in this case light intensity, should also be recorded along with the plant data.

The results can then be represented on a kite diagram.

Exam tip

There are two important principles that must be taken into account when sampling populations:

- The sample must be large enough so that the data are **representative** of the population as a whole.
- The sample should be taken at random so that the data are **unbiased**.

Knowledge check 29

The data below show the number of buttercups recorded in a $0.25\,m^2$ quadrat.

Quadrat number	Number of buttercup plants
1	2
2	7
3	9
4	5
5	8
6	1
7	4
8	6
9	3
10	4

Use the data to calculate the mean number of buttercups:

a per quadrat

b per m^2

Summary

After studying this topic you should be able to demonstrate and apply your knowledge and understanding of:

- the concept of an ecosystem
- the pattern of population growth in both natural and controlled environments
- the effect that density-dependent factors and density-independent factors have on population growth
- the principle of ecological succession — both primary and secondary succession
- decomposition and its importance to the ecosystem in the recycling of mineral nutrients
- the transfer of energy through ecosystems, from the Sun to primary producers, primary consumers and secondary consumers
- the carbon cycle, linking the processes of photosynthesis, respiration, decomposition, fossilisation and combustion
- the effects of human activities on the carbon cycle, leading to global warming and climate change
- the role of bacteria in the nitrogen cycle and the significance of nitrogen to living organisms
- the economic importance of the nitrogen cycle in food production
- the effects of human activities on the nitrogen cycle, including the use, and misuse, of inorganic fertilisers

Human impact on the environment

Endangered species and conservation

Extinction is a natural process — the majority of species that have ever existed are now extinct. The majority of these extinctions have occurred due to natural phenomena, such as natural selection. It is now apparent that our own species has been, and is continuing to be, responsible for a reduction in biodiversity.

Knowledge check 30

What is meant by the term biodiversity?

The effects of human activities on the environment can be broadly divided into four categories:

- **Habitat destruction** — for example, deforestation of tropical rainforests, the removal of hedgerows and drainage of wetlands in the UK.
- **Pollution** — including greenhouse gas emissions, oil, pesticides (e.g. DDT) and inorganic fertilisers.
- **Over-hunting** — this ranges from the hunting of large game (e.g. black rhino) to the over-exploitation of fish, such as blue-fin tuna. As a result both of these species are endangered.
- **Competition from non-native and domestic species** — many species have been introduced to areas where they didn't evolve, for example the grey squirrel and Japanese knotweed have been introduced into the UK. Without their natural predators or pathogens their populations increase and they out-compete native species, causing their numbers to decline. Domestic species, such as goats and donkeys, have been selectively bred and they can also out-compete 'wild' species.

The aim of conservation is to maintain biodiversity, ensure the survival of endangered species and to conserve existing gene pools. For ethical reasons it is important to conserve potentially useful genes for future generations of humans as well as for the survival of the species itself. Each species' genes represent important human assets as they are a potential source of food, chemicals and medicines.

To try to reduce the impact on biodiversity, different conservation measures have been taken:

- **Habitat protection** creates nature reserves and SSSIs (Sites of Special Scientific Interest), where an entire ecosystem is protected.
- **International cooperation and treaties** can be used to restrict trade in endangered species and to reduce pollution. For example, CITES (Convention on International Trade in Endangered Species) has made the trade in rhino horn and whale meat illegal. The Kyoto Protocol is an international treaty, which commits governments to reducing greenhouse gas emissions.
- **Zoos** play an important role in the protection, and breeding, of endangered species. Many species, such as the Arabian oryx and the Californian condor, have been saved from extinction through breeding programmes. Zoos are also involved in the reintroduction of species, such as the Californian condor, back into the wild. The numbers of red kites in Wales and England have also risen due to reintroduction programmes. Some zoos are also establishing sperm banks and freezing the embryos of endangered animals in order to prevent extinction.
- Stocks of seeds of traditional varieties of plant are stored in **seed banks** at institutions such as the Royal Botanical Gardens at Kew.

Agricultural exploitation

Agricultural exploitation refers to the way in which food production has increased in efficiency and intensity to maximise the yield from the land in order to meet human needs. As human populations have increased so has the demand for food, which has led to conflicts between farming and conservation. There are two main aspects of modern agriculture that have had a dramatic impact on biodiversity:

- **Mechanisation** — to allow large machinery to manoeuvre effectively, larger fields have had to be created. This has led to the removal of hedgerows and consequently a reduction in biodiversity.
- **Monoculture** — this involves the growing of a single variety of crop over a large area of land, for example wheat. As the same crop is grown each year, the same nutrients are removed from the soil, which are then not replaced due to harvesting. This has led to an increased use of inorganic fertilisers, which can lead to eutrophication. Monoculture also provides ideal conditions for pest populations to increase, which has led to an increase in the use of **pesticides**. Many pesticides are non-selective and kill other organisms, such as pollinating insects, which leads to a reduction in biodiversity.

Deforestation

Deforestation is the *removal of trees over a large area*. Different factors are responsible for deforestation, and include:

- land cleared for subsistence farming and cash crops
- large-scale extraction of timber to be used in building

- land cleared to build roads to provide transport infrastructure
- wood used as fuel
- manufacture of paper and packaging

Deforestation has a number of environmental implications:

- The loss of habitat leads directly to a loss in biodiversity.
- The loss of valuable sources of plant chemicals that have potential benefits for humans.
- The presence of tree roots protects the soil, and much of the rainwater that falls on forests is taken up by trees during transpiration. The removal of trees therefore leads to increased soil erosion and flooding.
- Forests play a crucial role in regulating atmospheric carbon dioxide, by removing the gas during photosynthesis. It is estimated that global deforestation accounts for 30% of the increase in atmospheric CO_2.

It is essential that native woodlands, i.e. woodlands that have developed naturally due to the process of succession, are preserved. Native woodlands usually contain the highest biodiversity, as they provide a wide range of habitats for the species that live there.

However, there is still a demand for wood and wood products. In order to meet this demand forests must be managed to ensure that the timber is produced sustainably. These sustainable practices include the following:

- **Coppicing** — this involves the stems of young trees being repeatedly cut down to near ground level. The tree is not killed, and many new shoots start to grow from the stump. This process can be repeated over and over again, producing a reliable source of timber. Coppiced woodland always has a range of different-aged coppice growing in it, which provides a wide variety of habitats and leads to an increase in biodiversity.
- **Selective cutting** — where the oldest, largest trees are removed. This leaves the majority of the woodland intact, and therefore reduces the impacts of soil erosion.
- **Plantations** — where fast-growing species are planted, and when they are cut down new trees are planted. This ensures a long-term, sustainable supply of timber.

Overfishing

Overfishing occurs when the harvesting rate is higher than the birth rate. Therefore the population numbers decline. The continued fishing results in the capture of smaller, younger fish, so the breeding stock is unable to maintain previous population levels.

Figure 41 shows the numbers of cod caught in Canadian waters from 1850 to 2000. At the start of the 1960s the use of factory trawlers resulted in much greater numbers of fish being harvested. As a result the cod population collapsed and the fishery was closed in 1992.

There are international agreements in place to try to regulate fishing and make it **sustainable**, i.e. to allow the population level to be maintained indefinitely. These agreements involve:

- **increasing mesh size** of nets to enable smaller fish to escape, allowing them to reproduce
- enforcing **exclusion zones** to prevent fishing in overfished areas

Knowledge check 31

Explain two ways in which deforestation could lead to an increase in atmospheric carbon dioxide concentrations.

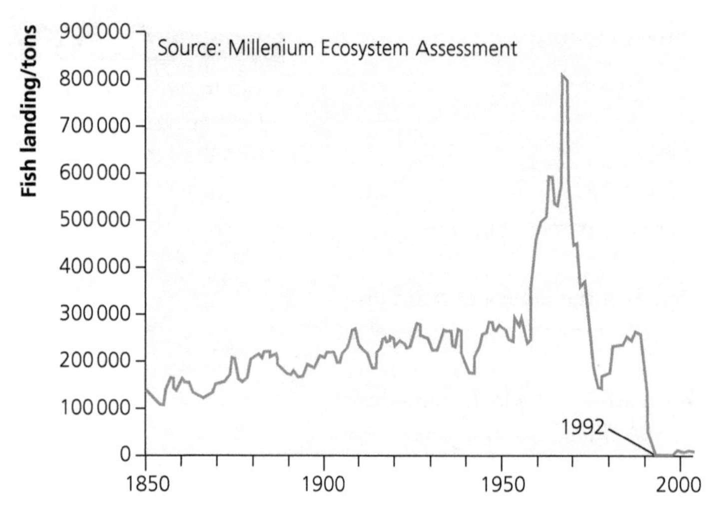

Figure 41 The number of cod caught in Canadian waters from 1850 to 2000

Knowledge check 32

Explain how an increase in the mesh-size of nets will help to reduce overfishing.

- enforcing **fishing seasons** to prevent fishing during the breeding season
- imposing fishing **quotas**, based on scientific estimates of the size of fish stocks

Fish farming can also reduce the pressure on wild stocks of fish, while still meeting human demands. However, it is an intensive farming practice and there are many problems associated with it. Fish are very densely stocked, encouraging the spread of pathogens and parasites, which may also spread to wild fish. To combat these problems antibiotics and pesticides are widely used, which can also harm marine invertebrates. The waste (ammonia and faeces) produced by the fish can cause increased nitrate concentrations, leading to eutrophication in the surrounding areas.

Planetary boundaries

The concept of planetary boundaries is relatively new and was developed by a group of international environmental scientists. Their research indicates that, since the Industrial Revolution, the activity of humans has become the main cause of global environmental change. They identified nine Earth system processes that possess boundaries, which if crossed may result in abrupt or irreversible environmental changes. However, remaining within these boundaries will allow human societies to continue to develop sustainably. The nine planetary boundaries are:

- climate change
- rate of biodiversity loss
- biogeochemical (the impact on global nitrogen and phosphorus cycles)
- ocean acidification
- land use changes
- global fresh water consumption
- ozone depletion
- atmospheric aerosols
- chemical pollution

Scientists have concluded that the first three boundaries have already been crossed. The concentration of atmospheric CO_2 shows no signs of reducing, and will therefore lead to further climate change. The current rate of extinction of species is comparable to those seen during the previous five mass extinction events, which all resulted in a major loss of species. Eutrophication, due to the increased use of inorganic fertilisers in modern agriculture, has induced abrupt changes in lake and marine ecosystems.

The scientists also concluded that humanity is at risk of crossing three other boundaries — those of ocean acidification, global fresh water consumption and land use changes. However, a reduction in deforestation, changes to farming practices and a reduction in the burning of fossil fuels may prevent these boundaries being crossed.

During the 1980s it became apparent that the release of CFCs into the atmosphere was resulting in a depletion of the stratospheric ozone layer. The Montreal Protocol was established and adopted by 46 governments committed to protecting the ozone layer. The resulting ban on CFCs and similar chemicals means that the ozone hole in Antarctica is slowly recovering and, consequently, the ozone boundary has not been crossed.

Due to the large variety of chemicals and particles in the environment it has been difficult to determine the planetary boundaries for chemical pollution and atmospheric aerosols. As such, these boundaries are unquantified, and further research is required to establish their effects on ecosystems.

Summary

After studying this topic you should be able to demonstrate and apply your knowledge and understanding of:

- the factors contributing to a reduction in biodiversity
- the strategies employed by organisations involved in the conservation of endangered species and existing gene pools
- the conflicts between the demand for food production and the need for conservation, including the effects of deforestation and overfishing
- management strategies that are required to ensure that human activities are sustainable
- the concept of planetary boundaries

Homeostasis and the kidney

Excretion of nitrogenous waste

Protein metabolism

Excretion is the removal of waste products of metabolism from the body. If allowed to build up inside cells and tissues these waste products can be toxic. The two main excretory products produced by animals are carbon dioxide, produced during aerobic respiration, and nitrogenous waste from the breakdown of excess amino acids (and nucleic acids).

When proteins are digested the amino acids absorbed into the body are used to synthesise other proteins, for example enzymes and hormones. Excess amino acids cannot be stored in the body. They are broken down in the liver by a process called **deamination** (Figure 42).

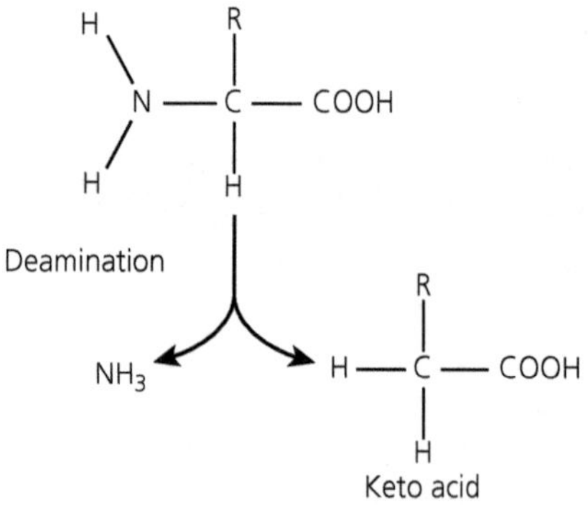

Figure 42 Deamination of excess amino acids

An amine group is removed from the amino acid and is then converted into ammonia. The remainder of the amino acid (now a keto-acid) is either respired or converted to carbohydrate or lipid to be stored.

Different types of nitrogenous waste

To excrete nitrogenous waste safely, water is used to dilute it to non-toxic levels. Nitrogenous waste is excreted in different forms: ammonia, urea and uric acid. The main form of nitrogenous waste excreted is dependent upon the availability of water within an animal's habitat and the extent to which water loss is controlled by the organism. However, all animals excrete all three to some extent.

Ammonia

Ammonia is a small, soluble and highly toxic molecule. It must be excreted immediately. It cannot be stored and requires large volumes of water to dilute it to non-toxic levels for it to be excreted safely.

Freshwater fish have body fluids that have a lower water potential than their surroundings and so they absorb large quantities of water by osmosis. Most of this water enters through their highly permeable gills. Freshwater fish therefore excrete ammonia as they have to remove a large volume of excess water. Some of the ammonia is excreted via the kidneys. However, as it is highly soluble, most of it diffuses from the gills.

Urea

Mammals excrete **urea**. Urea is much less toxic than ammonia and therefore can be stored for a period of time in the tissues. As it is less toxic it requires less water to dilute it down to safe levels.

Although producing urea is energetically expensive it is an adaptation to life on land and helps to prevent dehydration.

Uric acid

Reptiles, **birds** and **insects** excrete **uric acid**. Uric acid has low toxicity and can therefore be stored for long periods of time. Very little water is needed to store it and safely excrete it and it is removed from the bodies as a white paste. The low toxicity means that it can accumulate inside the eggs of birds and reptiles, without damaging the embryo.

Although producing uric acid is energetically expensive it allows these animals to survive in arid environments and reduces their mass, which is an advantage for flight.

Summary of nitrogenous waste types

Figure 43 summarises the different excretory products and the relative (energy) cost and volume of water needed to excrete them safely.

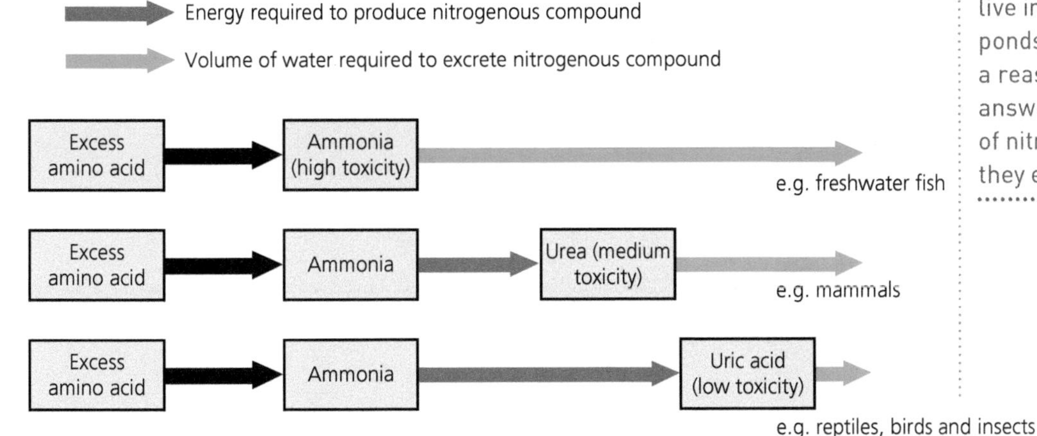

Figure 43 The excretion of different forms of nitrogenous waste

The mammalian kidney

In mammals, deamination of amino acids occurs mainly in the liver. The ammonia produced is quickly converted to urea in the **ornithine** cycle. The urea then diffuses into the blood where it is removed by the kidneys.

The mammalian kidney performs two main functions: the **excretion of urea** and the regulation of the water potential of the blood (**osmoregulation**). Although mammals excrete urea, the mammalian kidney shows adaptations for controlling water loss and there is a correlation between the availability of water in the environment and the animal's ability to conserve water.

Exam tip

If you are given a question about the different excretory products of animals you need to take into account the type of animal involved (and if its embryo developed inside an amniote egg) and the availability of fresh water in its environment. The lower the toxicity of the molecule, the longer it can be stored and the less water is required to excrete it safely.

Knowledge check 33

Red-eared terrapins live in freshwater ponds and lakes. Giving a reason for your answer, state what type of nitrogenous waste they excrete.

Gross anatomy of the urinary tract

- The kidneys are located in the abdominal cavity.
- They receive oxygenated blood from the renal artery.
- The urine produced in the kidney travels to the bladder via the ureter.
- The internal anatomy of the kidney is divided into two main regions — the inner medulla and the outer cortex (Figure 44).

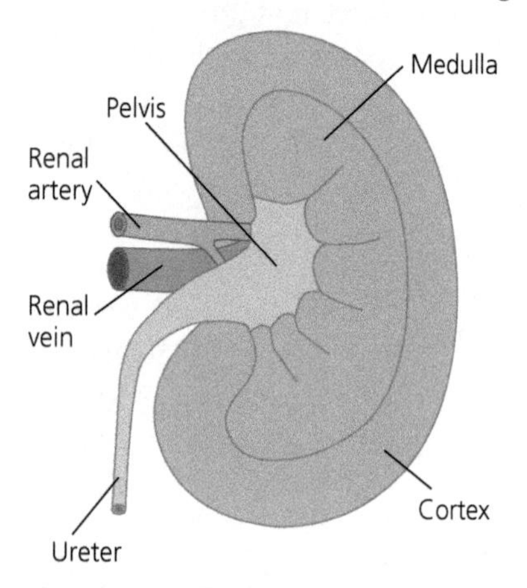

Figure 44 The gross structure of the kidney

Exam tip

Synoptic link to biological molecules: Unlike most organs, the kidneys are not protected by the skeleton. They are protected by a thick layer of fat tissue that surrounds the delicate organ.

The nephron

Each kidney has an estimated 1 million nephrons (Figure 45) providing a large surface area for the exchange of materials. The nephron has four functional regions:

- the Bowman's capsule and glomerulus
- the proximal convoluted tubule
- the loop of Henle
- the distal convoluted tubule and collecting duct

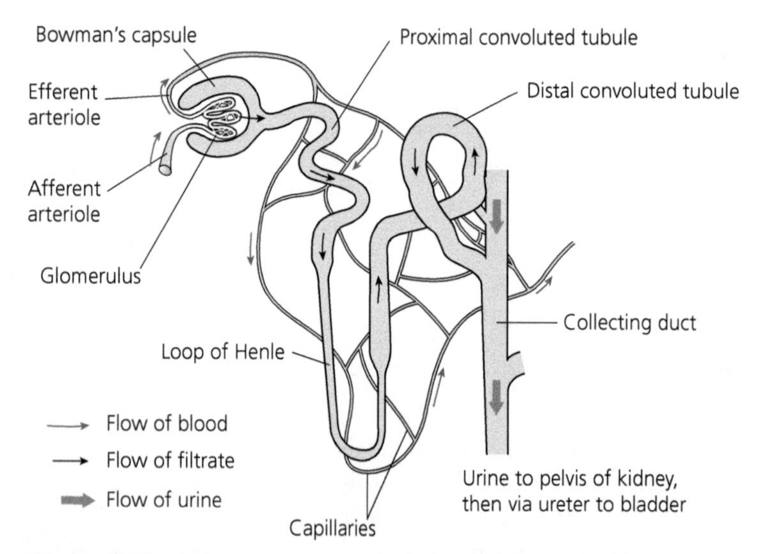

Figure 45 The kidney nephron and associated blood vessels

Exam tip

The nephron is the functional unit of the kidney. As the basic structure of all nephrons is the same the function of the kidney can be explained by looking at what happens along the length of one nephron.

The Bowman's capsule and glomerulus

Ultrafiltration is the removal of water and small solutes from the blood and the formation of fluid called the glomerular filtrate. It takes place between the capillaries of the glomerulus and the Bowman's capsule (Figure 46).

The capillary walls of the glomerulus are made up of a single layer of endothelial cells with pores between them, called fenestrations, making the capillaries highly permeable.

The basement membrane surrounding the capillary acts as a **molecular filter**:

- Water and small solutes are forced out of the blood and into the capsular space.
- Blood cells and large solutes, such as plasma proteins, are prevented from leaving the capillaries.

The inner layer of the Bowman's capsule is composed of cells called **podocytes**, which have 'foot-like' processes that wrap around the capillaries.

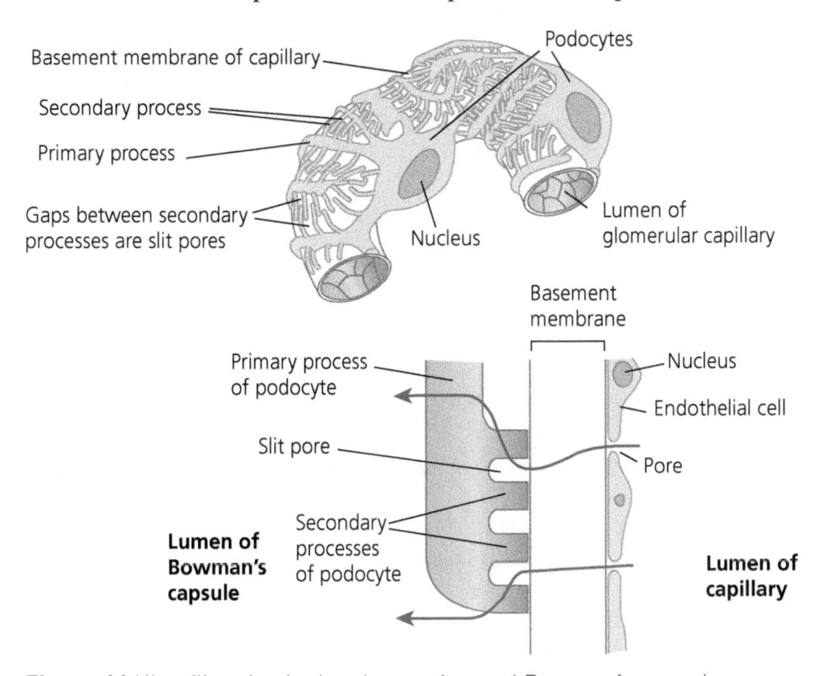

Figure 46 Ultrafiltration in the glomerulus and Bowman's capsule

The **hydrostatic pressure** of the blood in the glomerulus is very high due to:

- contraction of the left ventricle (the renal artery branches from the aorta)
- the efferent arteriole leaving the glomerulus being narrower than the afferent arteriole, which produces a 'bottleneck' effect

The hydrostatic pressure forces fluid (water and small solutes) through the endothelium and the basement membrane, and down through the spaces between the podocytes into the lumen of the Bowman's capsule. This fluid is now called the **(ultra)filtrate**.

The rate of ultrafiltration is high — about 125 cm^3 of filtrate is produced every minute.

Exam tip

Afferent means 'to bring to' and efferent means 'to carry away'. Both terms are used in anatomy to describe structures such as blood vessels and neurones. When describing ultrafiltration you will need to use these terms. To help you get them the right way round think of the alphabet: **a** comes before **e** just as **a**fferent comes before **e**fferent.

The proximal convoluted tubule

The proximal convoluted tubule is the longest region of the nephron and is composed of a single layer of cuboidal epithelial cells adapted for the **selective reabsorption** of solutes (Figure 47). These cells:

- possess microvilli to provide a large surface area for reabsorption via carrier proteins
- contain many mitochondria to provide the ATP for active transport of solutes

The peritubular capillaries are close to the tubule, providing a short diffusion pathway for reabsorption. Over 80% of the filtrate is reabsorbed here, including all of the glucose and amino acids and most (approximately 85%) of the sodium ions. Some urea (about 50%) passes back into the blood by facilitated diffusion. The reabsorption of these solutes, along with the presence of plasma proteins (which remained in the blood), lowers the water potential of the blood in the capillaries surrounding the tubule. As a result, most of the water (about 85%) in the filtrate is reabsorbed by osmosis.

The reabsorption of glucose and amino acids from the filtrate is dependent upon the **co-transport** of sodium ions (Figure 47). The plasma membrane nearest to the capillaries is highly folded to form numerous intercellular spaces. The Na^+/K^+ pump within these membranes *drives* the reabsorption of solutes:

1. The Na^+/K^+ pump actively transports Na^+ out of the epithelial cell and into the intercellular spaces. This reduces the concentration of Na^+ inside the epithelial cell, generating a concentration gradient between the lumen of the nephron and the cytoplasm of the epithelial cell.
2. As a result Na^+ and glucose (or a specific amino acid) bind to carrier proteins and enter the cell by facilitated diffusion.
3. The concentration of glucose, and amino acids, increases inside the cytoplasm of the epithelial cell so these pass into the blood via facilitated diffusion. Facilitated diffusion is a relatively slow process, so some of these molecules are absorbed by active transport. This ensures that all of the glucose and amino acids are absorbed from the lumen of the nephron.

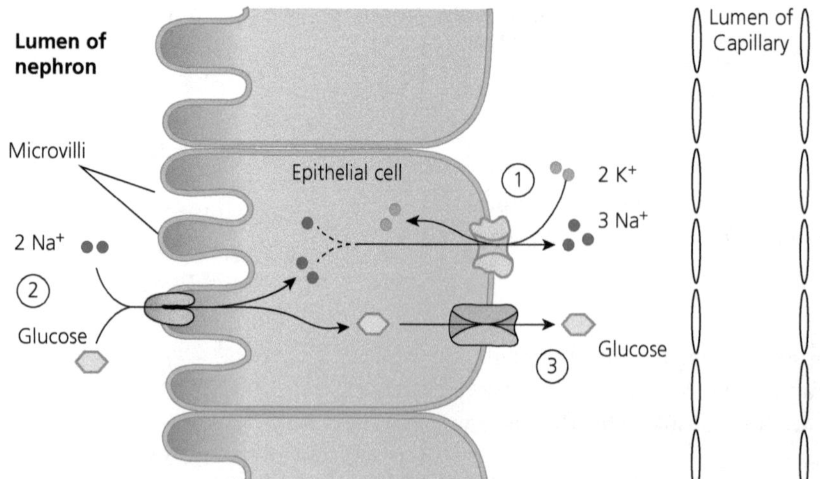

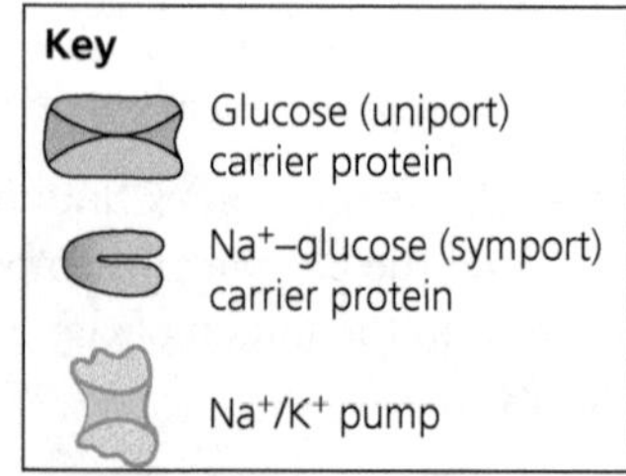

Figure 47 Selective reabsorption via an epithelial cell from the proximal convoluted tubule

Knowledge check 34

Explain why the pressure in the glomerular capillaries is higher than capillaries found elsewhere in the body.

Knowledge check 35

a Name three substances that will normally be present in the filtrate.

b Name an additional substance that may be present in the filtrate of a person with high blood pressure.

Exam tip

Synoptic link to cell membranes: Selective reabsorption involves active transport, facilitated diffusion and osmosis. It would be advisable to revisit your notes from A-level year 1 to ensure that you fully understand these mechanisms. This will also help with your understanding of nerve impulses.

The loop of Henle and collecting duct

The function of the loop of Henle is to conserve water. This results in the production of concentrated urine, i.e. urine that has a higher solute concentration and lower water potential than the blood.

The concentration of urine produced is related directly to the length of the loop of Henle — the longer the loop the greater the volume of water reabsorbed (conserved).

- The kidneys of semi-aquatic mammals, such as the beaver, have short loops of Henle and produce a large volume of dilute urine.
- The kidneys of desert-dwelling mammals, such as the kangaroo rat, have long loops of Henle and produce a small volume of concentrated urine.

The structure of the loop of Henle can be divided into:

- the descending limb, which is highly permeable to water
- the ascending limb, which is highly permeable to ions but relatively impermeable to water

Walls of the vasa recta (blood capillaries) surrounding the loop are freely permeable to both water and ions.

Generation of water potential gradients

The function of the ascending limb is to create a water potential gradient between the filtrate and the tissue fluid of the medulla. It achieves this by the **active transport** of sodium and chloride ions (from the filtrate) into the medulla (**1** in Figure 48). This increases the concentration of ions, and lowers the water potential of the tissue fluid of the medulla (**2**). This causes water to move out of the filtrate from the descending limb (**3**) by **osmosis** (due to the ascending limb being

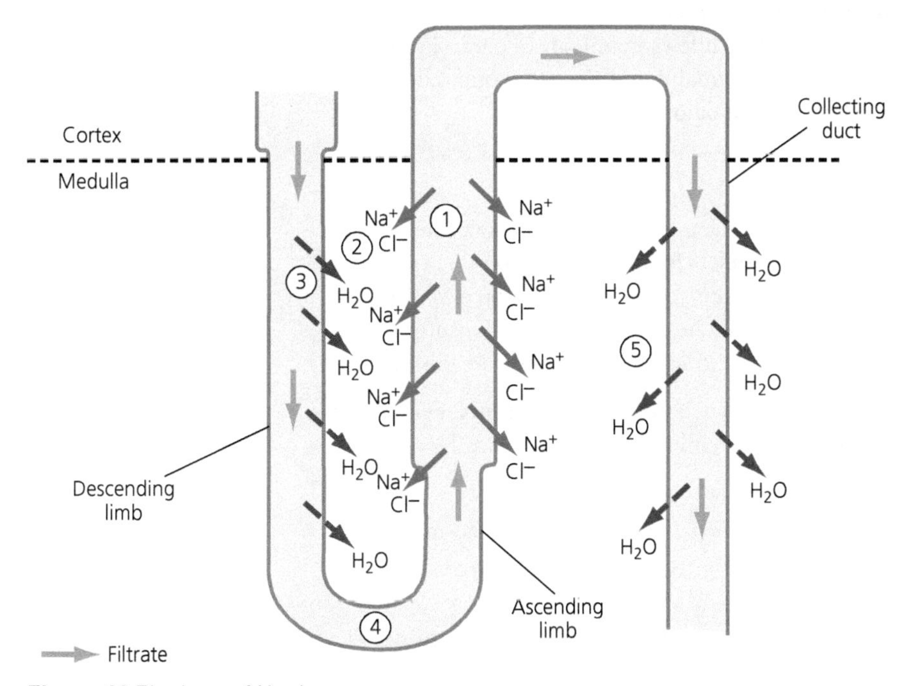

Figure 48 The loop of Henle

Exam tip

Synoptic link to adaptations for nutrition: The reabsorption of glucose and amino acids, from the lumen of the nephron, involves cotransport with sodium ions. The same mechanism is involved in the absorption of these molecules from the lumen of the gut.

Knowledge check 36

Describe two ways in which the cells from the proximal convoluted tubule are adapted for reabsorption.

Knowledge check 37

Explain the difference in the length of the loop of Henle in an otter and a camel.

impermeable to water). The water is reabsorbed into the vasa recta and removed so that it does not dilute the tissues (i.e. increase the water potential) of the medulla.

This process is repeated down the length of the loop so that:

- As the filtrate moves down the descending limb it loses water, causing it to have a higher ion concentration (i.e. become more concentrated) and lower water potential.
- As the filtrate moves up the ascending limb it loses ions, causing it to have a lower ion concentration (i.e. become more dilute) and higher water potential.
- At the apex of the loop (**4**) the filtrate reaches a maximum ion concentration.

The loop of Henle acts as a **countercurrent-multiplier** system. Countercurrrent refers to the fact that the filtrate flows in opposite directions in the loop, down the descending limb and up the ascending limb. The multiplier effect refers to the generation of the solute gradient (and therefore a water potential gradient) in the medulla. This gradient is caused by ions being pumped out of the ascending limb. The effect of the pump is multiplied due to ions being constantly removed from the filtrate in the ascending limb and being replaced as the filtrate flows through the proximal convoluted tubule and the descending limb.

The reabsorption of water

As the filtrate enters the distal convoluted tubule it has a higher water potential than the tissues of the medulla.

As the filtrate moves down the collecting duct it once again meets tissue fluid with a lower water potential as a result of the pumping of solutes from the ascending limb of the loop of Henle. Therefore, water moves out of the filtrate by osmosis along the entire length of the collecting duct (**5** in Figure 48) and is reabsorbed into the blood. This produces urine that is greatly reduced in volume and has a much lower water potential than blood (i.e. is concentrated).

The permeability of the walls of the distal convoluted tubule and collecting duct are affected by **antidiuretic hormone** (ADH). This allows mammals to control the volume of water reabsorbed into the blood and so maintain the water potential of the blood at a relatively constant value. This is called **osmoregulation**.

Knowledge check 38

Name the part of the nephron that provides the water potential gradient for the reabsorption of water from the collecting duct.

Homeostasis

The term **homeostasis** is used to describe the mechanisms that bring about the maintenance of a **constant internal environment**. Homeostasis is important to ensure that the conditions inside cells remain at the optimum for them to function effectively independently of the external environmental conditions. Homeostasis also ensures that optimum conditions are maintained, regardless of the activity level of the organism.

Homeostasis is brought about by both the **nervous** and **endocrine systems**. Features of an organism's internal environment have a set optimum level, also known as the norm.

Figure 49 shows the homeostatic process involving:

- a **receptor** (detector), which detects a stimulus (i.e. change from the norm)
- a **coordinator**, which receives information from the receptor and initiates the corrective mechanism
- an **effector**, which carries out the corrective procedure to restore the norm

In most biological systems a **negative feedback** system operates to maintain the norm. Negative feedback means that any change from the norm will bring about a corrective mechanism to restore the norm.

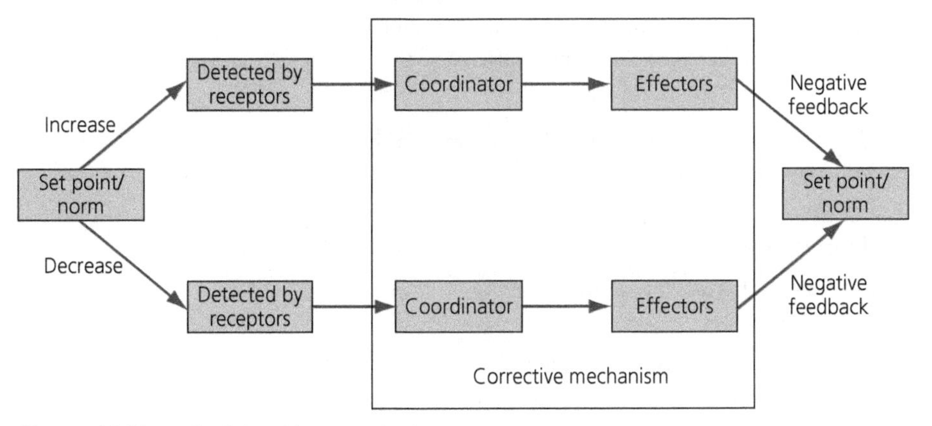

Figure 49 The principle of homeostasis

An efficient homeostatic mechanism ensures that the factor being controlled shows minimal fluctuation around a set point.

Osmoregulation

Osmoregulation is the control of the water content and solute composition of the blood. The body maintains the water potential of the blood at an approximately steady state by balancing water uptake from the diet with water loss by sweating, evaporation from the lungs, and in urine and faeces. Figure 50 summarises the process of osmoregulation.

Exam tip

If you are asked to describe the process of homeostasis you need to make reference to following: the norm, the receptor/detector, the coordinator, the effector, the corrective actions and negative feedback.

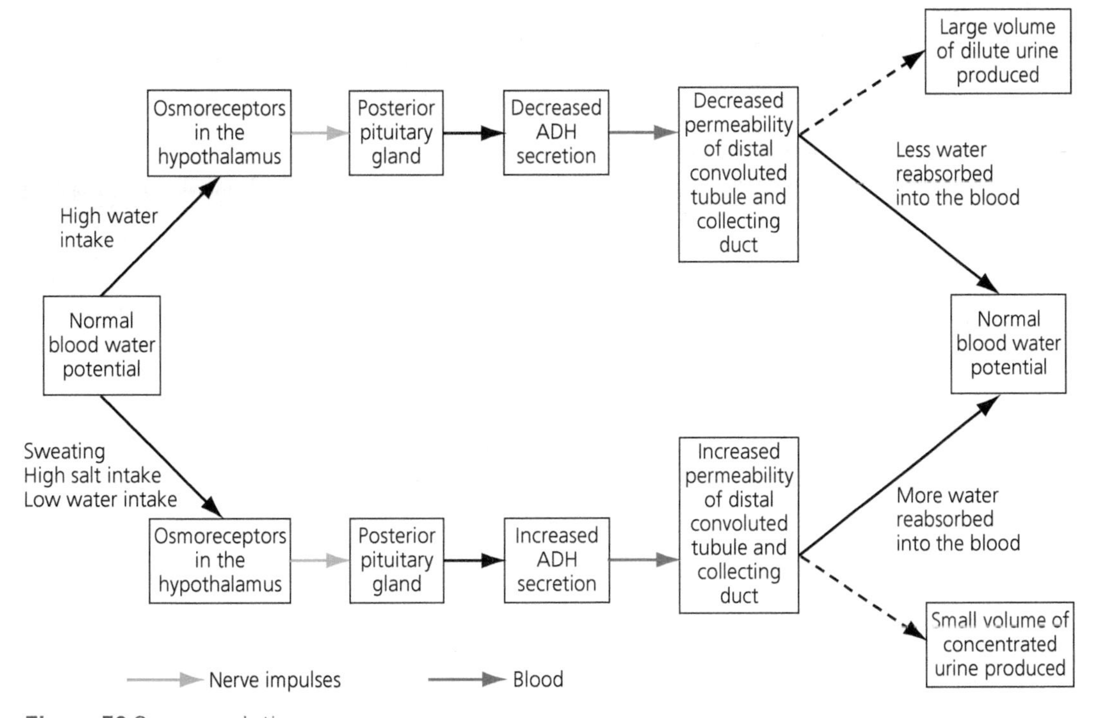

Figure 50 Osmoregulation

Osmoregulation is under endocrine control. The posterior lobe of the pituitary gland secretes the hormone **ADH** (antidiuretic hormone), which affects the reabsorption of water from the filtrate in the nephron. ADH binds to receptors on the surface of the cells and causes aquaporins, located in the cytoplasm, to migrate and become incorporated into the plasma membranes. This *increases* the **permeability** of the walls of the collecting duct and distal convoluted tubule to water.

The water potential of the blood *falls* when the diet contains too little water (or a high intake of solutes) or during periods of excessive sweating:

1. The decrease in water potential of the blood is detected by **osmoreceptors** located in the **hypothalamus**.
2. Nerve impulses are generated and pass to the **posterior pituitary gland**, which responds by secreting *more* **ADH**.
3. The ADH travels in the bloodstream and on reaching the kidneys brings about *increased* permeability of the walls of the distal convoluted tubules and collecting ducts of the nephrons.
4. This results in more water being reabsorbed into the blood from the filtrate.
5. This restores the normal water potential of the blood and results in the production of a small volume of hypertonic urine.

The water potential of the blood *rises* when the diet contains too much water (or a low intake of solutes):

1. The increase in water potential of the blood is detected by osmoreceptors located in the hypothalamus.
2. Fewer nerve impulses are generated and the posterior pituitary gland responds by secreting *less* ADH.
3. This *decreases* the permeability of the walls of the distal convoluted tubules and collecting ducts of the nephrons.
4. This results in less water being reabsorbed into the blood from the filtrate.
5. This restores the normal water potential of the blood and results in the production of a large volume of hypotonic urine.

Knowledge check 39

Name the receptor (detector), coordinator and effector involved in osmoregulation.

Kidney failure

When the kidneys are damaged by injury or infection the solute concentration and water potential of the blood and other body tissues is affected. This can also lead to the accumulation of waste products in the blood.

People with kidney failure are advised to follow a protein-controlled diet and a low salt (sodium chloride) intake. A diet high in protein will result in higher concentrations of urea in the blood due to an increase in deamination of excess amino acids. A high-protein diet may also lead to increased concentrations of uric acid being produced, which will lower the pH of the blood plasma. This may lead to a disorder known as gout, and to the production of kidney stones. A high intake of sodium chloride also places greater demands on the kidney, as it has to remove the excess ions. It also results in higher blood pressure, which will increase the rate of ultrafiltration.

Although it is possible to survive with only one functional kidney, failure of both is fatal if untreated. Treatment of kidney failure may involve kidney dialysis or a kidney transplant.

Dialysis

Haemodialysis is a method of removing excess fluid and solutes, such as urea, from the blood, effectively replacing the excretion functions of failed kidneys. The kidney machine works on the principle of countercurrent exchange. Blood from the patient is pumped through the machine in one direction, while solution, called dialysate, is pumped through the machine in the opposite direction. The two fluids are separated by an artificial membrane that allows exchange to occur. The artificial membrane will allow small solutes, such as urea, to pass through, but will prevent the passage of larger molecules and cells.

The movement of molecules is purely passive and relies on diffusion of molecules down concentration gradients. The composition of the dialysate is therefore carefully controlled. To prevent the loss of useful molecules, such as glucose, the dialysate's composition is the same as that of normal blood plasma. However, the concentration of waste molecules, such as urea, is much lower than normal blood plasma, facilitating its removal from the blood.

In **peritoneal dialysis** the dialysis solution is introduced into the peritoneal cavity, in the abdomen. The membrane surrounding the abdominal cavity, the peritoneum, acts as a natural filter and allows the exchange of solutes between the blood plasma and the dialysate. After a certain period of time the dialysate, containing waste solutes such as urea, is drained from the peritoneal cavity.

Kidney transplant

Although dialysis is effective, the treatment needs to be repeated regularly, and patients spend considerable time connected to the dialysis machine. Patients must ensure that they stick to a rigid diet, and there are risks of anaemia and infection from continued dialysis.

Kidney transplantation is by far the best treatment for kidney failure. This procedure involves the removal of a healthy kidney from a human donor, inserting it into the body of the patient and connecting it to the recipient's blood supply and urinary bladder. Donors tend to be close relatives, as the antigens on the surface of their cells are similar. This decreases the chances of the donor kidney being rejected by the recipient. Immunosuppressant drugs are also given to the recipient to inhibit the activity of the cells of the immune system, again decreasing the chances of tissue rejection.

Practical work

During this topic you should have completed a kidney dissection. This will have allowed you to view the two main regions of the kidney, the medulla and cortex, as shown in Figure 44 on p. 54.

The different structures of the nephron can be seen when sections of the kidney are viewed with an optical microscope. Figure 51a shows a section through the cortex. The Bowman's capsule, glomerulus and the proximal and distal convoluted tubules are clearly visible. Figure 51b shows a section through the medulla, with the loop of Henle and collecting duct clearly visible.

→

Knowledge check 40

Explain why the haemodialysis is more effective with the blood and dialysate passing in opposite directions (countercurrent flow) than in the same direction (parallel flow).

Exam tip

Peritoneal dialysis is less effective than haemodialysis as an equilibrium will be established between the blood plasma and the dialysate. As a result less urea will be removed from the blood.

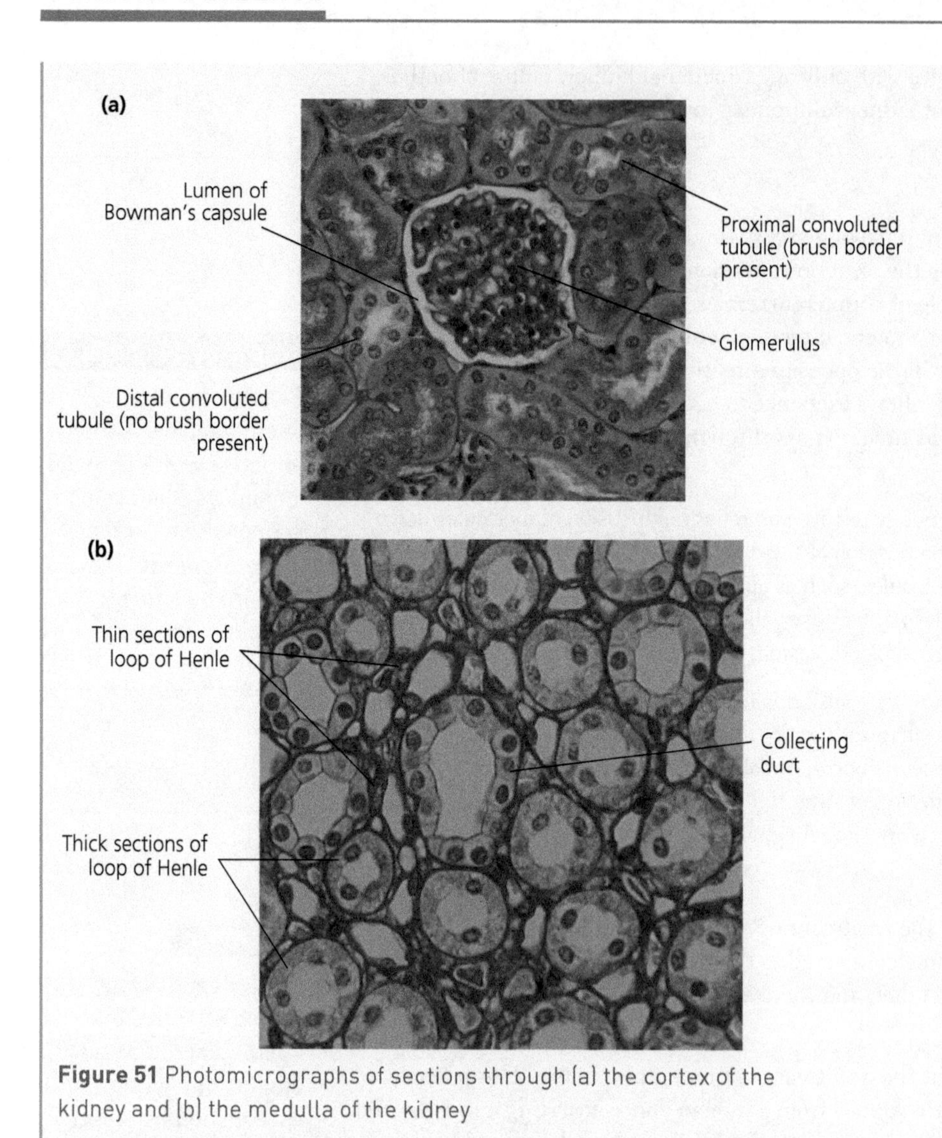

Figure 51 Photomicrographs of sections through (a) the cortex of the kidney and (b) the medulla of the kidney

Exam tip

Many students have difficulty interpreting photomicrographs such as the ones shown in Figure 51. However, if you think about the biology you have learned you should be able to arrive at the correct answer. You have probably drawn a nephron, including the boundary between the cortex and the medulla. You will remember that the Bowman's capsule, glomerulus, proximal and distal convoluted tubules are in the cortex and that the medulla only contains the loop of Henle and collecting duct.

Summary

After studying this topic you should be able to demonstrate and apply your knowledge and understanding of:

- the need for different animals to produce different excretory products
- the different regions of the mammalian kidney
- the structure and function of the nephron and associated blood supply in relation to:
  - ultrafiltration
  - selective reabsorption
  - the production of urine hypertonic to blood plasma
- the adaptations of the loop of Henle in organisms in different environments
- the concept of homeostasis and its importance in maintaining a constant internal environment
- negative feedback, and its importance in restoring conditions to their optimum levels
- the role of the posterior pituitary gland and the role of antidiuretic hormone in regulating the water potential of the blood
- the effects and treatment of kidney failure

The nervous system

Organisms increase their chances of survival by responding to **stimuli**. These stimuli include:

- temperature
- light intensity/wavelength/duration
- chemicals — these may cause, for example, particular smells or pH changes

A **stimulus** is a change in an organism's internal or external environment.

These stimulus–response control systems always follow the same basic pattern (Figure 52).

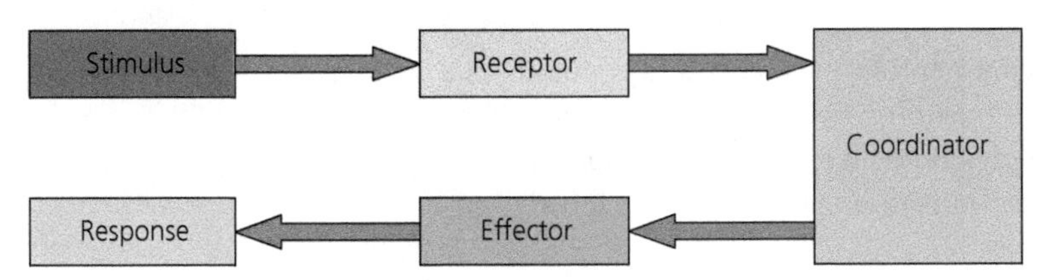

Figure 52 The stimulus–response control system

The mammalian nervous system

The individual components of the stimulus–response control system in a mammal are receptor–coordinator–effector.

- **Receptors** are specialised sensory cells that detect internal or external stimuli. They act as transducers by converting one form of energy into electrochemical energy. For example, photoreceptors in the retina convert light energy into electrochemical energy.
- The **coordinator** is the central nervous system (CNS) and is composed of the brain and spinal cord. It processes the information received from receptors and initiates the appropriate response by communicating with effectors.
- **Effectors** are muscles or glands. They bring about the response.

The **peripheral nervous system** is composed of the individual neurones and ganglia that connect the receptors and effectors to the CNS.

Neurones and nerve pathways

Neurones are highly specialised cells that link together to form pathways (Figure 53). There are three basic types:

- **sensory neurones** — transmit impulses from receptors to the CNS
- **motor neurones** — transmit impulses from the CNS to effectors
- **relay neurones** — link sensory and motor neurones in the CNS

Knowledge check 41

Give the names of two different types of effector.

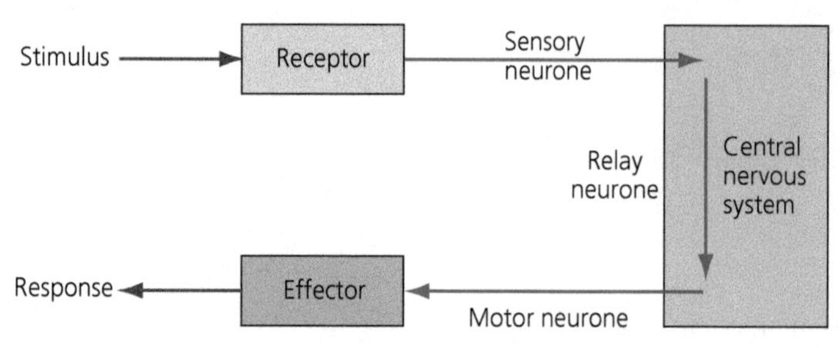

Figure 53 The neural pathway involved in responding to a stimulus

The motor neurone

Figure 54 shows the structure of a typical motor neurone. The **cell body** contains the nucleus and most of the cell's other organelles including ribosomes, which synthesise neurotransmitters, and mitochondria, which provide ATP for the sodium and potassium ion (Na^+/K^+) pump. The **dendrites** transmit impulses to the cell body; the **axon** transmits impulses away from the cell body.

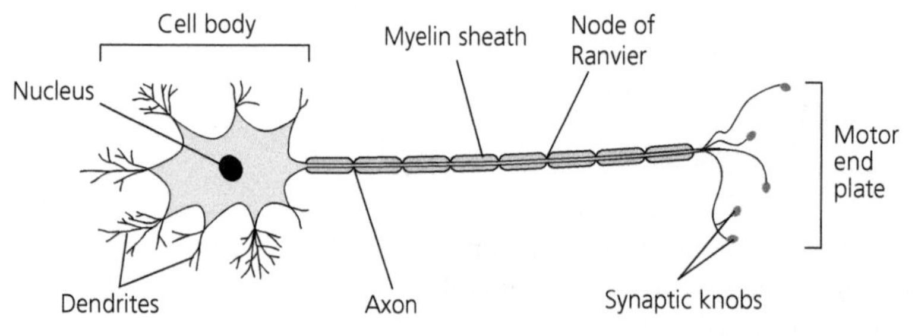

Figure 54 A myelinated motor neurone

Some vertebrate neurones are surrounded and insulated by a fatty **myelin sheath**. This is formed by **Schwann cells**. During myelination the membrane of the Schwann cell becomes extended and wraps itself around the axon (Figure 55). Schwann cells also secrete a fatty material called myelin. The combination of the membrane phospholipids and the myelin — the myelin sheath — insulates the neurone by preventing the movement of ions into and out of the axon. There are small gaps between the Schwann cells called **nodes of Ranvier**. Here the axon is 'exposed', which allows the movement of ions into and out of the axon. Myelination occurs only in the vertebrate nervous system.

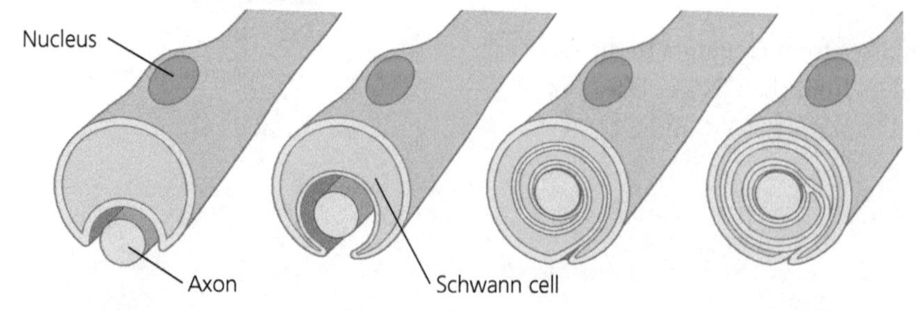

Figure 55 A Schwann cell wrapping around a neurone during myelination

Exam tip

A nerve and a neurone are not the same structure. A nerve is a bundle of neurones surrounded by a protective sheath of fibrous tissue; a neurone is an individual nerve cell. Most of the content here is about neurones. You must make sure that you refer to them correctly.

Knowledge check 42

What is the difference in function between an axon and a dendrite?

Pre-existing knowledge

Membrane structure

- Membranes are composed mainly of phospholipids and proteins.
- The phospholipids form a bilayer and the hydrophobic core prevents the passage of polar molecules and ions.
- Extrinsic proteins occur on only one side of the membrane; intrinsic proteins span the entire membrane.
- Intrinsic proteins are involved in the transport of polar molecules and ions across the membrane via facilitated diffusion and active transport.
- Facilitated diffusion involves the movement of molecules or ions down a concentration gradient and is a passive process.
- Active transport involves the movement of molecules or ions against a concentration gradient and requires energy from the hydrolysis of ATP.

The nature of the nerve impulse

Nerve impulses are **electrochemical** in nature and are the result of a potential difference across the membrane of the neurone. The nature of the nerve impulse was discovered by investigating the giant axons of squid. By inserting microelectrodes into the axon and the fluid surrounding the axon, the potential difference can be measured. Changes in the potential difference can be monitored using a cathode-ray oscilloscope (Figure 56).

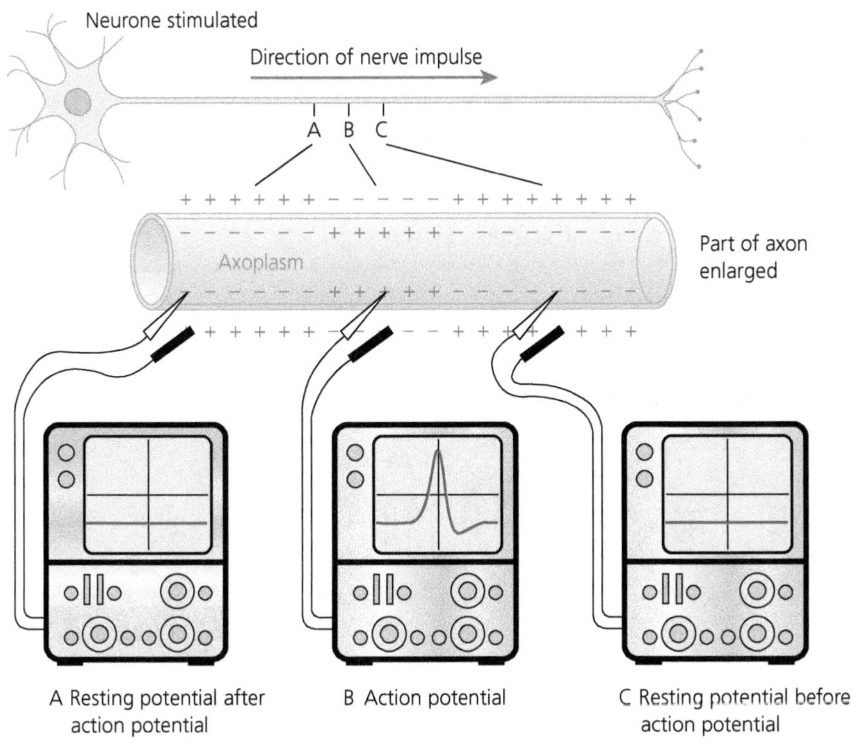

Figure 56 Changes in potential difference across neuronal membranes are detected using microelectrodes and displayed on oscilloscopes

Structure of the axon membrane

The nerve impulse is based on the movement of sodium ions (Na^+) and potassium ions (K^+) across the membrane of the axon. The Na^+ and K^+ ions are transported across the membrane by both active transport and facilitated diffusion. Figure 57 shows the different types of intrinsic proteins involved with this:

- Na^+/K^+ pump, which requires energy from the hydrolysis of ATP
- K^+ channels (relatively many)
- voltage-gated Na^+ channels
- voltage-gated K^+ channels

There are also Na^+ channels. As they are relatively few in number, these are not shown in Figure 57.

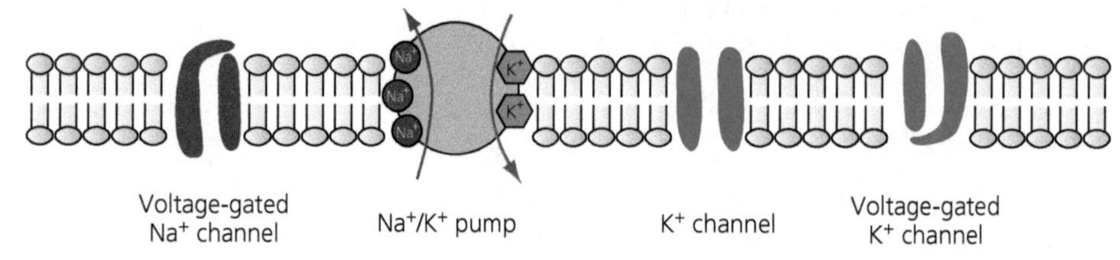

Figure 57 Structure of the neurone membrane

The resting neurone

Axons have a differing permeability to Na^+ and K^+ ions. The membrane is more permeable to K^+ ions than to Na^+ ions. This is due to the relative abundance of K^+ channel proteins.

The generation of the resting potential is illustrated in Figure 58. The Na^+/K^+ ion pump actively transports Na^+ ions *out* of the neurone and K^+ ions *into* the neurone. For every three Na^+ ions pumped out, only two K^+ ions are pumped in. As a result, concentration gradients are established across the membrane. The axon membrane is highly permeable to K^+ ions, which diffuse rapidly out of the neurone. However, because the membrane is relatively impermeable to Na^+ ions, they can only diffuse back into the neurone slowly.

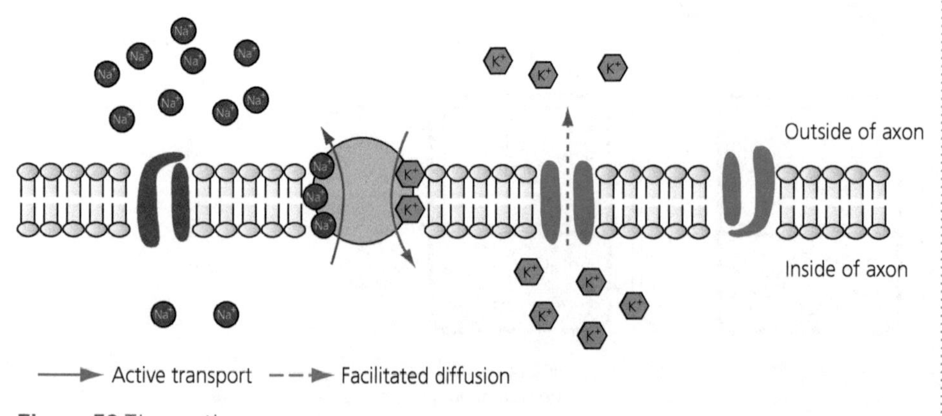

Figure 58 The resting neurone

Knowledge check 43

Describe how a resting potential is maintained in a neurone.

The overall outward movement of ions establishes a potential difference across the membrane. The inside of the axon is negatively charged (relative to the outside) and the membrane is said to be **polarised**. At rest, the potential difference is **–70 mV**. This is called the **resting potential**.

The active neurone

Figure 59 illustrates how an action potential is generated. When the neurone is stimulated, the voltage-gated Na^+ ion channels open, which increases the permeability of the membrane to Na^+ ions. Na^+ ions diffuse rapidly into the axon, which **depolarises** the membrane. The potential difference across the membrane is briefly reversed, becoming positive (+40 mV) on the inside. This change in polarity (i.e. when the inside of the axon is positive) is known as an **action potential**.

Knowledge check 44

Describe how the potential difference changes when a neurone is stimulated.

Exam tip

Nerve impulses, depolarisations and action potentials — what's the difference? The axon membrane depolarises when the potential difference across the membrane rises from it polarised state (–70 mV). An action potential is produced when the inside of the axon becomes positively charged.

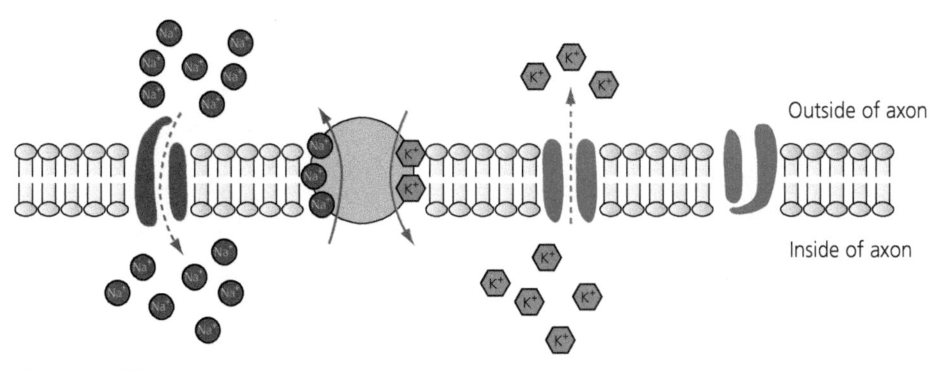

Figure 59 The active neurone

At the end of depolarisation the voltage-gated Na^+ ion channels close and the permeability of the membrane to Na^+ ions decreases. The membrane starts to **repolarise** and the voltage-gated K^+ ion channels open. This temporarily increases the permeability of the membrane to K^+ ions, increasing the rate of their outward diffusion (Figure 60).

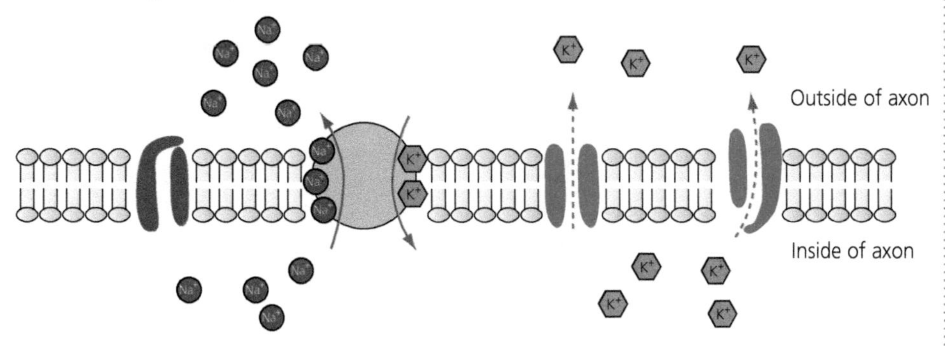

Figure 60 Repolarising the membrane

Due to the increased permeability to K^+ ions the potential difference across the membrane 'overshoots' the resting potential to −80 mV. The neurone is **hyperpolarised**. The voltage-gated K^+ ion channels then close and the Na^+/K^+ ion pump restores the resting potential of the membrane.

Figure 61 shows the changes in potential difference and conductance (permeability) of the axon membrane to Na^+ and K^+ ions during the passage of an action potential. It shows that the depolarisation of the membrane coincides with the increase in permeability of the membrane to Na^+ ions. It can also be seen that the repolarisation coincides with an increased permeability to K^+ ions.

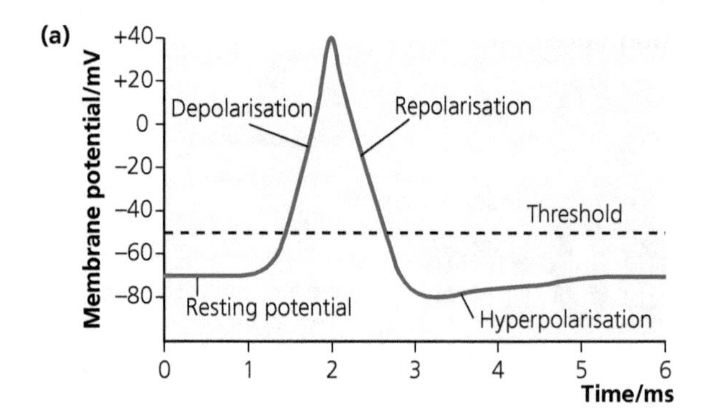

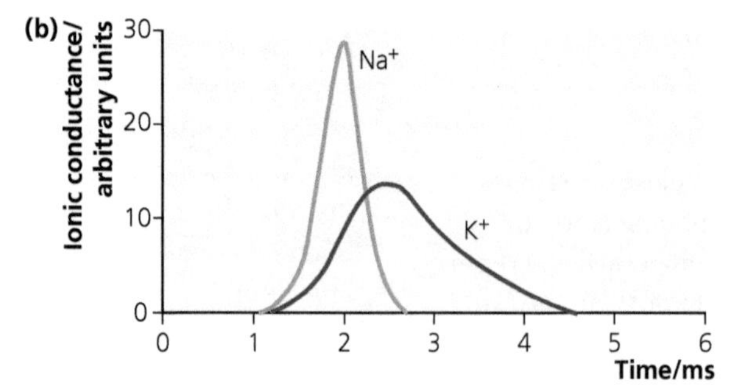

Figure 61 The change in (a) potential difference and (b) the conductance of Na^+ and K^+ ions during the passage of an action potential

The threshold

For an action potential to be generated the depolarisation must exceed a **threshold value**, which is usually 10–15 mV above the resting potential (Figure 61a). A **threshold stimulus** is a stimulus that is sufficient to set up an action potential in a neurone. Any stimulus weaker than the threshold (a sub-threshold stimulus) will not generate an action potential. Above the threshold, the size or strength of the action potential is always the same irrespective of the size or strength of the stimulus. This is known as the **all-or-nothing law**. The frequency of action potentials is directly related to the intensity of the stimulus, i.e. the greater the intensity of stimulus the greater is the frequency of action potentials.

The refractory period

For a brief period following an action potential the voltage-gated Na^+ channels are inactivated and the inward movement of Na^+ ions is prevented. Therefore another action potential cannot be generated; this is known as the **refractory period**. The refractory period ensures that:

- an action potential can be propagated in one direction only
- a second action potential is separated from the first, which limits the frequency of action potentials along a neurone

The propagation of a nerve impulse

Once an action potential has been set up it moves rapidly from one end of the neurone to the other. The movement is the result of local electrical currents set up by the ion movements of the action potential itself. This is illustrated in Figure 62.

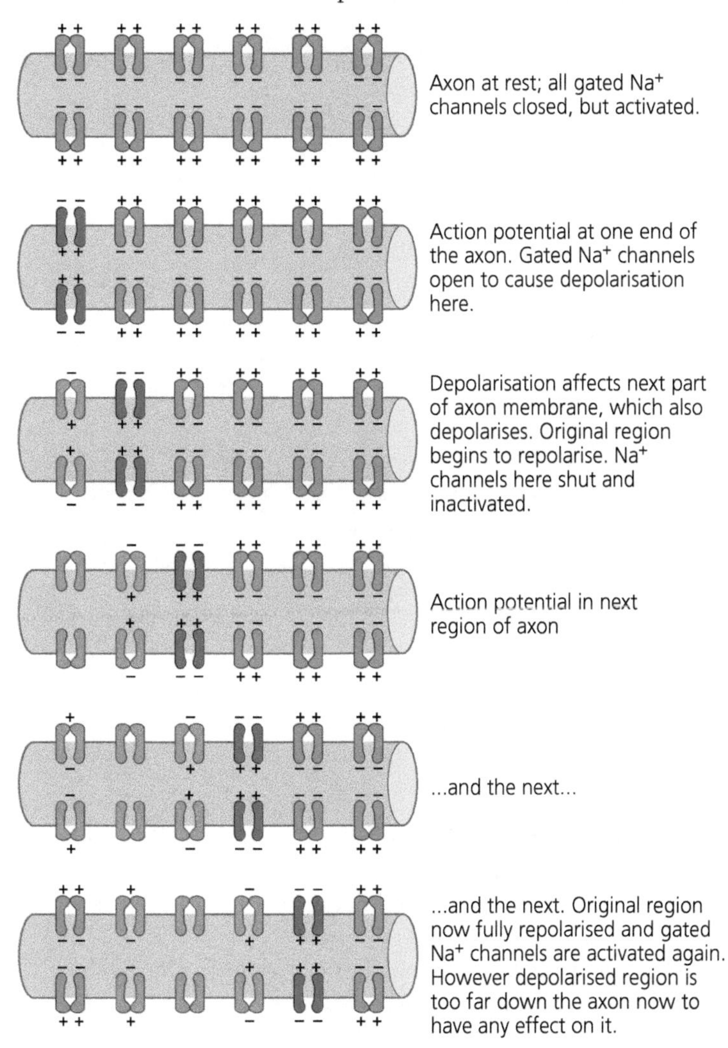

Figure 62 Propagation of an action potential along a non-myelinated neurone

1 When the neurone is stimulated Na^+ ions rush into the axon, depolarising the membrane (see second diagram). This creates an area of positive charge and a flow of current is set up in a **local circuit** between this active area and the negatively charged resting region immediately in front of it.
2 The current flow in the local circuit partially depolarises the membrane ahead of the active region. This causes gated Na^+ channels to open, allowing an influx of Na^+, which fully depolarises the membrane (see third diagram).
3 Behind the impulse, K^+ ions begin to leave, causing the neurone to become repolarised behind the impulse.

Repeated depolarisations of immediately adjacent regions results in a step-by-step wave of action potentials along the entire length of the neurone. It can also be seen that the gated Na^+ channels are inactivated behind the impulse (i.e. during the refractory period). By the time they are activated again (bottom diagram) the action potential is too far down the axon to affect the area where the action potential originated. This explains how the refractory period ensures that impulses travel in one direction only.

Speed of the impulse

The speed of the impulse varies from approximately $1\,m\,s^{-1}$ to $100\,m\,s^{-1}$ depending upon three factors:

- the temperature
- the diameter of the axon
- the presence or absence of a myelin sheath

Temperature

As the temperature increases to about 40°C the speed of transmission increases. The generation of nerve impulses is an active process and requires ATP from respiration. Therefore, anything that affects the rate of respiration (such as temperature) affects the speed of transmission. This explains why endothermic animals have faster responses than ectothermic animals.

Diameter of the axon

The speed of propagation of an action potential depends upon the distance the current can flow in the local circuit — the greater the length of the circuit, the faster the speed of propagation.

The length of the local circuit is influenced by the longitudinal resistance of axoplasm (cytoplasm in the axon); the greater the longitudinal resistance the shorter the local circuit. By increasing the diameter of the axon the longitudinal resistance of the axoplasm is reduced. With lower resistance the current can flow further along the axon membrane, increasing the length of the local circuit. This increases the distance between adjacent depolarisations, which in turn increases the speed of propagation.

This explains why marine invertebrates, such as squid, which live at temperatures close to 0°C, have developed thick axons to speed up their responses.

Myelination

The **myelin sheath** acts as an electrical insulator. Ions cannot pass through it. The sheath is interrupted by **nodes of Ranvier**. It is only at these points that local circuits are set up, allowing the movement of Na^+ and K^+ ions across the membrane. This effectively increases the distance over which the local currents can bring about depolarisation. It causes the action potential to 'jump' from node to node and increases the speed of transmission. This process is known as **saltatory conduction** (Figure 63).

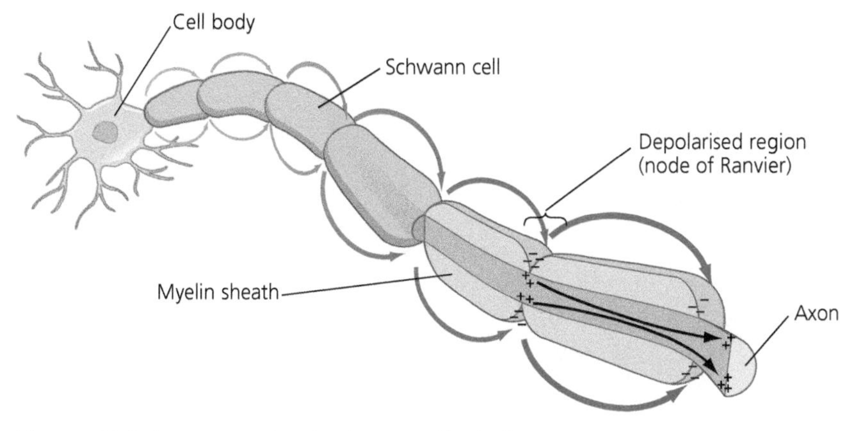

Figure 63 Saltatory conduction in a myelinated neurone

Synapses

A **synapse** is a junction, 20 nm in width, between two neurones. The transmission of the impulse from one neurone to the next is by chemicals called **neurotransmitters**. There are two main types of neurotransmitter:

- **acetylcholine** (ACh), which is produced by motor neurones targeting muscle cells
- **noradrenaline**

Other neurotransmitters include dopamine and serotonin.

Structure of the synapse

Figure 64 shows the structure of a synapse. At the end of the neurone, the axon swells to form the **synaptic knob**. This contains **synaptic vesicles** containing the neurotransmitter and many mitochondria to produce ATP for the resynthesis of neurotransmitter molecules and the Na^+/K^+ pumps.

Synaptic transmission

Figure 65 shows how an impulse is transmitted across a (cholinergic) synapse. The nerve impulse reaches the synaptic knob (**1** in Figure 65) and depolarises the presynaptic membrane, causing voltage-gated calcium ion channels to open (**2**). Calcium ions diffuse into the presynaptic neurone causing the synaptic vesicles to move towards and fuse with the presynaptic membrane (**3**) where they release acetylcholine into the synaptic cleft via exocytosis (**4**).

The acetylcholine diffuses across the synaptic cleft (**5**) and binds with specific receptor proteins on the postsynaptic membrane (**6**). The receptor proteins are

Exam tip

A nerve impulse refers to the movement of action potentials along a neurone. It is important that when describing the transmission of a nerve impulse you clearly state that the **action potentials** move along the neurone or that **action potentials** jump from node to node.

Exam tip

As the Na^+/K^+ pumps are only active at the nodes of Ranvier, myelinated neurones use less ATP than non-myelinated neurones.

Knowledge check 45

Describe the effect of the following on the speed of transmission of a nerve impulse:

a the presence of a myelin sheath
b an increase in axon diameter

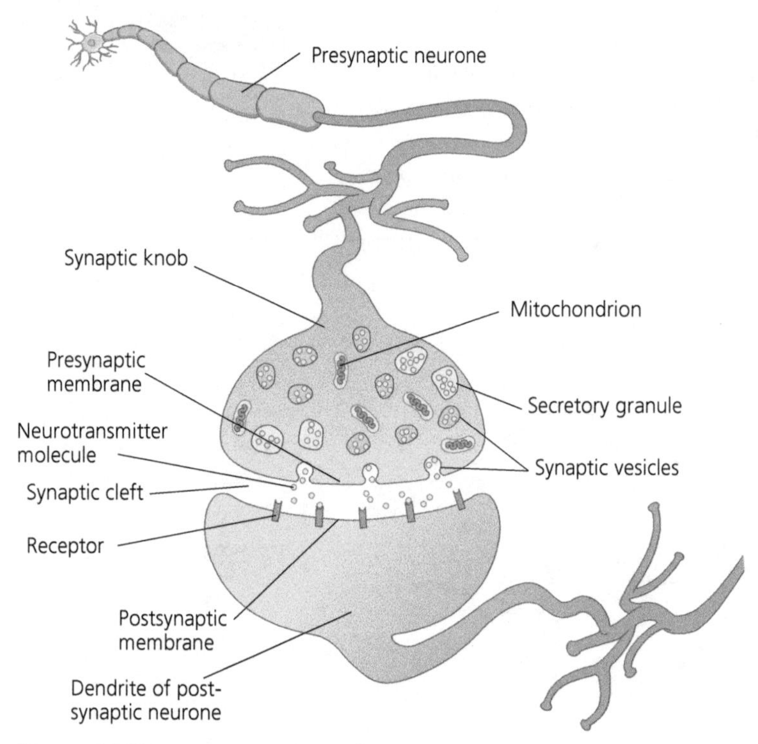

Figure 64 The structure of a cholinergic synapse

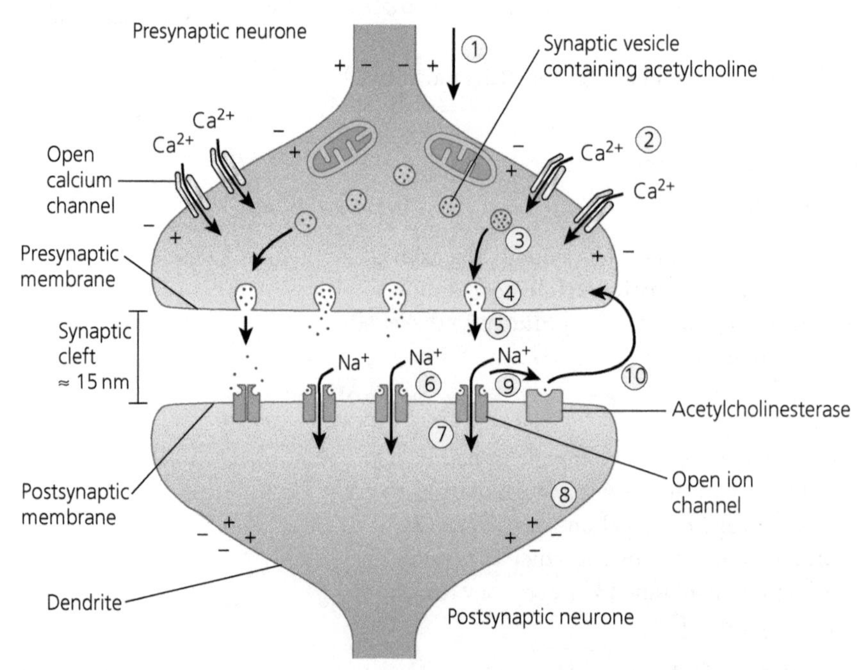

Figure 65 Transmission of an impulse across a cholinergic synapse

attached to gated Na^+ channels; the binding of acetylcholine causes the protein to change shape and the Na^+ channels to open. Na^+ ions diffuse into the postsynaptic neurone (**7**). If the threshold is reached an action potential is generated in the postsynaptic neurone (**8**).

Once the acetylcholine has depolarised the postsynaptic neurone it is hydrolysed by the enzyme acetylcholinesterase, which is located on the postsynaptic membrane (**9**). This prevents successive impulses merging at the synapse. The resulting molecules (choline and ethanoic acid) diffuse back across the synaptic cleft and are actively transported back into the synaptic knob of the presynaptic neurone (**10**). Energy released from the hydrolysis of ATP is required to reform the acetylcholine, which is then stored in the synaptic vesicles.

Knowledge check 46

State two reasons why mitochondria are present in the synaptic knob.

Functions of synapses

Synapses transmit impulses in **one direction only** (unidirectional):

- The neurotransmitter is released only from the presynaptic neurone.
- The neurotransmitter receptors are found only on the postsynaptic membrane.
- Neurotransmitter diffuses from the presynaptic neurone to the postsynaptic neurone.

Synapses **filter out low-level stimuli**. If the intensity of a threshold stimulus is low then the frequency of impulses sent along a neurone is low. Only a small quantity of neurotransmitter is released and few Na^+ channels open on the postsynaptic membrane. This may be insufficient to exceed the threshold value, in which case no action potential is generated in the postsynaptic neurone.

Synapses act as junctions and allow **summation** to occur. When several impulses arrive at a synapse a large quantity of neurotransmitter is released. This causes many gated Na^+ channels to open. The threshold is exceeded and an action potential is generated in the postsynaptic neurone.

There are two types of summation:

- **Temporal summation** — high-frequency impulses arrive in quick succession from the same presynaptic neurone and lead to an accumulation of neurotransmitter in the synapse.
- **Spatial summation** (Figure 66) — several impulses arrive at the same time from several different presynaptic neurones.

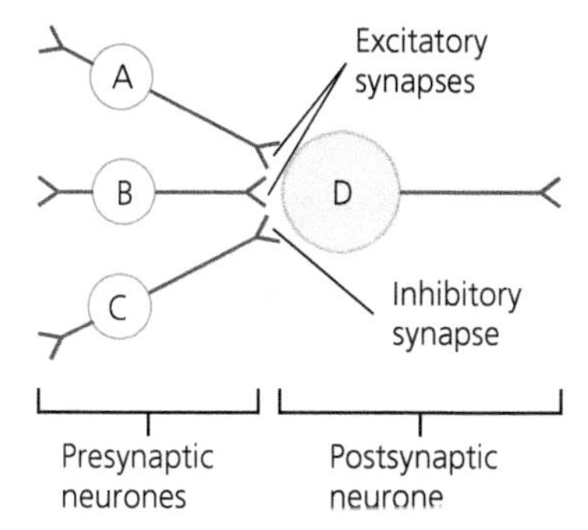

Figure 66 Spatial summation

Some synapses prevent the passage of impulses between neurones. **Inhibitory synapses** cause hyperpolarisation to occur in the postsynaptic membrane. This prevents an impulse being generated in the postsynaptic neurone. (See also the section on spinal reflexes, p. 75.)

Knowledge check 47

Explain two reasons why nerve impulses can only travel in one direction.

The effect of drugs on synaptic transmission

Most drugs that affect the nervous system influence synaptic transmission. Drugs fall into two broad categories: excitatory drugs (agonists) and inhibitory drugs (antagonists).

Excitatory drugs may have a similar shape to the neurotransmitter and bring about the same effect. They may inhibit the enzyme that breaks down the neurotransmitter, which results in the neurotransmitter remaining attached to the postsynaptic membrane. Examples are organophosphorous insecticides — they inhibit cholinesterase so acetylcholine remains bound to the postsynaptic membrane.

The significance is that agonists bring about continuous stimulation of the postsynaptic neurone/muscle. This can result in paralysis or death due to continuous contraction of cardiac and intercostal muscles.

Inhibitory drugs can bind to and block the receptors on the postsynaptic membrane. This prevents the neurotransmitter molecules from binding and prevents their action. Beta blockers are an example.

Inhibitory drugs can cause paralysis or death due to the inability of the muscles to contract.

Psychoactive drugs alter brain function and result in temporary changes in perception, mood, consciousness and behaviour. They include tobacco, cannabis, ecstasy, cocaine, heroin and amphetamines (speed).

Cocaine is an excitatory drug that works by preventing the normal re-uptake of the neurotransmitter dopamine. Dopamine accumulates in synapses, causing repeated action potentials in postsynaptic neurones. Dopamine stimulates the pleasure centres of the brain, giving a sense of wellbeing and happiness. Cocaine results in the overstimulation of the pleasure centres and the user feels euphoric.

Knowledge check 48

Organophosphorous insecticides are used to kill pests. Explain how the pesticide affects synaptic transmission.

The molecule THC is the active ingredient in marijuana. THC is an inhibitory drug that binds to receptors in the presynaptic membranes, thereby inhibiting the release of excitatory neurotransmitters. This prevents stimulation of the postsynaptic membranes, so a person intoxicated with marijuana is likely to feel relaxed and calm.

Reflexes

- **Reflexes** are not under the conscious control of the brain and are therefore **involuntary**.
- The neurones forming the pathway taken by the nerve impulses in a reflex action make up a **reflex arc**.
- Reflexes generally have a **protective function** and increase an organism's chances of survival.

A **reflex** is a rapid, automatic (involuntary) response to a particular stimulus.

The position of the spinal cord within the vertebral column is shown in Figure 67. When the spinal cord is viewed in a transverse section it shows two distinct regions:

- the central grey matter, which contains the **cell bodies** and relay neurones
- the outer white matter, which contains **myelinated axons** that run up and down the spinal cord to and from the brain

Sensory neurones transmit impulses from receptors to the CNS. They enter via the dorsal root and have their cell bodies in a swelling called the dorsal root ganglion.

Motor neurones transmit impulses from the CNS to effectors. They leave via the ventral root.

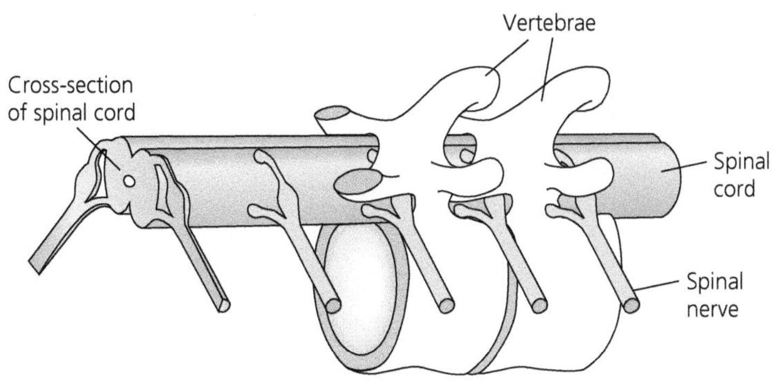

Figure 67 The position of the spinal cord within the vertebral column

Knowledge check 49

Explain why white matter is white and grey matter is grey.

Figure 68 shows a withdrawal reflex.

1. Heat from the hot plate is detected by a heat receptor in the finger.
2. An action potential is generated and an impulse is transmitted along a sensory neurone to the spinal cord via the dorsal root.
3. The sensory neurone synapses with a relay neurone in the grey matter of the spinal cord. The release of neurotransmitter by the sensory neurone generates an action potential in the relay neurone.
4. This is repeated at the synapse between the relay neurone and the motor neurone (also within the grey matter of the spinal cord). The action potential is transmitted along the motor neurone, via the ventral root, to the biceps muscle.
5. The release of acetylcholine causes the biceps muscle to contract, resulting in an automatic withdrawal of the hand from the hot plate.

Knowledge check 50

For the reflex in Figure 68 complete the following table:

Stimulus	
Receptor	
Coordinator	
Effector	
Response	

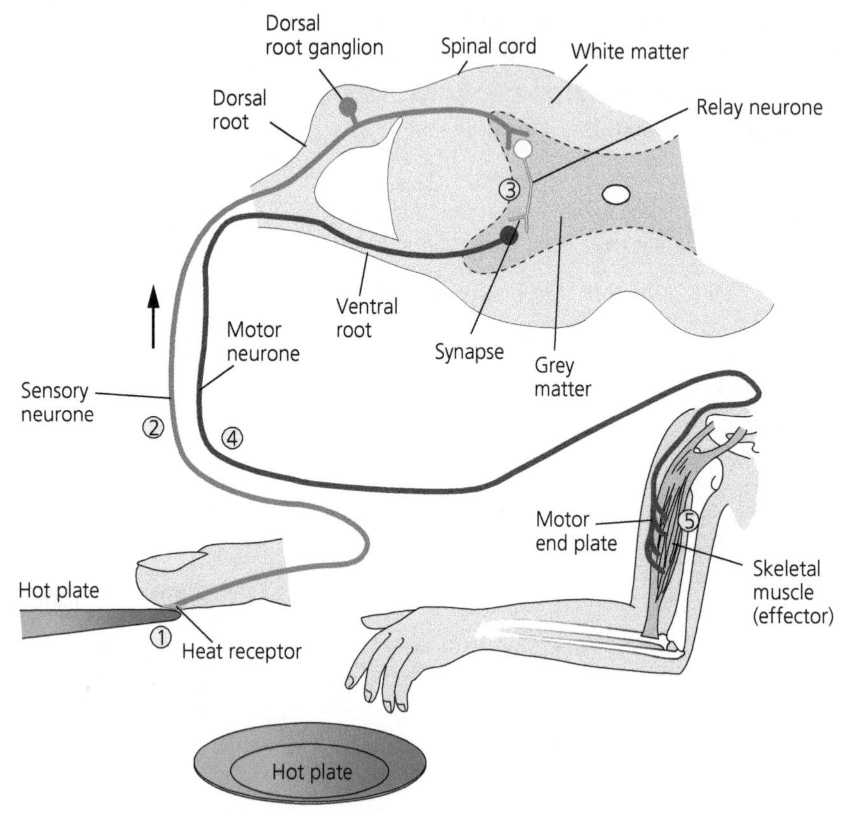

Figure 68 A section through the spinal cord and the pathways formed by the neurones in the withdrawal reflex

Exam tip

Many students have difficulty when completing a diagram to show the arrangement of neurones in a reflex arc. The sensory neurone *always* enters via the dorsal root; this is the one with the 'lump' in it (the dorsal root ganglion) where the cell body of the sensory neurone is located. The synapses *always* occur in the grey matter. The motor neurone *always* leaves via the ventral root. Always remember to label your diagrams.

Reflex arcs are not separate, and impulses can travel up and down the spinal cord. In the grey matter the sensory neurone may synapse with another neurone transmitting impulses to the brain. The information received may be stored in memory, which leads to learning.

The brain may relate the information received with other sensory input — for example, from the eyes — to modify the response. For example, if a hot metal dish is picked up it will probably be dropped immediately (simple spinal reflex). However, if an equally hot glass dish is picked up it will probably be put down quickly, but gently. In this second situation if the glass dish is dropped it may break and cause further harm to the individual. The brain makes a conscious decision and transmits impulses down the spinal cord via neurones that terminate in inhibitory synapses, which prevents the dish from being dropped immediately.

Nerve nets

Hydra is a simple organism that belongs to the phylum Cnidaria, which also contains sea anemones and jellyfish. They do not have a recognisable brain or true muscles. They have a **nerve net** (Figure 69), which is a simple system compared with the mammalian nervous system. **Photoreceptors** and **touch-sensitive nerve** cells are located in the body wall and tentacles. Therefore they respond to a limited number of stimuli — light intensity and touch. As a result, the numbers of effectors is small.

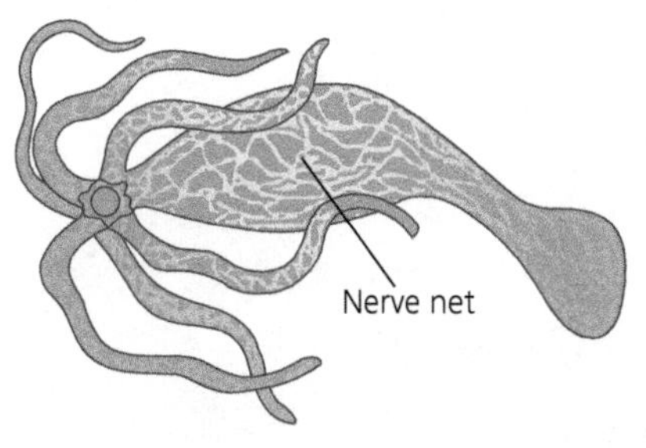

Figure 69 The structure of a nerve net in the Cnidarian *Hydra*

The nerve net consists of simple nerve cells with short extensions joined to each other and branching in a number of different directions. This means that the transmission of the nerve impulse is slow.

Knowledge check 51

Complete the following table to compare the structure and function of the neurones found in the nerve net of a jellyfish (Cnidarian) and those in a vertebrate.

Nerve net	Vertebrate neurones
Only one type of neurone	
	Neurones are longer
Neurones branched	
	Neurones can transmit impulses in one direction only
Impulses pass in all directions from point of stimulation	
	Neurones may be myelinated
Many synapses involved	
Slower transmission of impulses	

Summary

After studying this topic you should be able to demonstrate and apply your knowledge and understanding of:

- the response to a stimulus requiring information from a receptor to be relayed to an effector
- the structure and function of a mammalian motor neurone
- the nature and transmission of a nerve impulse, including the analysis of oscilloscope traces
- the factors that affect the speed of conduction of a nerve impulse
- the structure and function of a synapse in the transmission of information between neurones
- the effect of chemicals such as organophosphates and psychoactive drugs on synaptic transmission
- the structure of the spinal cord and how a simple reflex arc acts as the basis of protective, involuntary actions
- differences between the mammalian nervous system and the nerve net of a simple organism, such as *Hydra*

Questions & Answers

The exam(s)

You will be assessed through a range of structured questions. 9 marks are available for an extended response question that will be assessed for the quality of written communication in addition to meeting the scientific demands of the question.

When exam papers are being prepared, the examiner must try to ensure that all the topics covered in the unit are assessed, so you should be prepared to get questions from each of the topic areas. However, it would be impossible for examiners to ask a question on every topic. It is possible, therefore, that questions on the importance of ATP could be asked as part of a question on respiration or photosynthesis. Likewise, a question on human impact on the environment could be incorporated into a question on population size and ecosystems.

Examiners must also set questions that test the specific assessment objectives, so you may find it useful to understand the weighting of the assessment objectives that will be used:

Assessment objective	Brief summary	Approximate percentage of marks available
AO1	Demonstrate knowledge and understanding of scientific ideas, processes, techniques and procedures	30
AO2	Apply knowledge and understanding of scientific ideas, processes, techniques and procedures	45
AO3	Analyse, interpret and evaluate scientific information, ideas and evidence, including in relation to issues, to make judgments and reach conclusions and to develop and refine practical design and procedures	25
Total		**100**

Almost half the marks available target AO2 (apply knowledge and understanding of scientific ideas, processes, techniques and procedures) and many of the questions will be written in an unfamiliar context. However, it is important for you to understand that you should have learned all of the biology to enable you to answer these questions. First you need to recognise which part of the specification the question is targeting and then you should apply your knowledge to the particular scenario that has been presented. You may find it useful to use a highlighter pen to select the important information provided, because this will help you when you have to refer back to the stem of the question. For the WJEC Unit 3 exam there is a greater weighting of marks for AO3 compared with the Unit 1 and Unit 2 papers.

The exams will assess both your knowledge of practical biology and your mathematical skills. It is therefore important that you review your practical work, and practise doing calculations as part of your revision to ensure you gain the marks on these questions.

About this section

This section contains questions that are written in the style of the questions in the exam(s), so they will give you an idea of what you will be asked to do in the exam. Each question is followed by tips on what you need to do to gain full marks (shown by the icon ⓔ). The student responses are also followed by comments. These are preceded by the icon ⓔ and highlight where credit is due. In the weaker answers they also point out areas for improvement, specific problems and common errors, such as lack of clarity, irrelevance, misinterpretation of the question and mistaken meanings of terms.

Each question is attempted by two students — student A gives a weaker answer and student B gives a strong answer. Their answers, along with the comments, should help you to see what you need to do to score a good mark — and how you can easily not score a good mark even though you probably understand the biology.

Question 1 Photosynthesis

(a) The electron micrograph in shows a section through two chloroplasts.

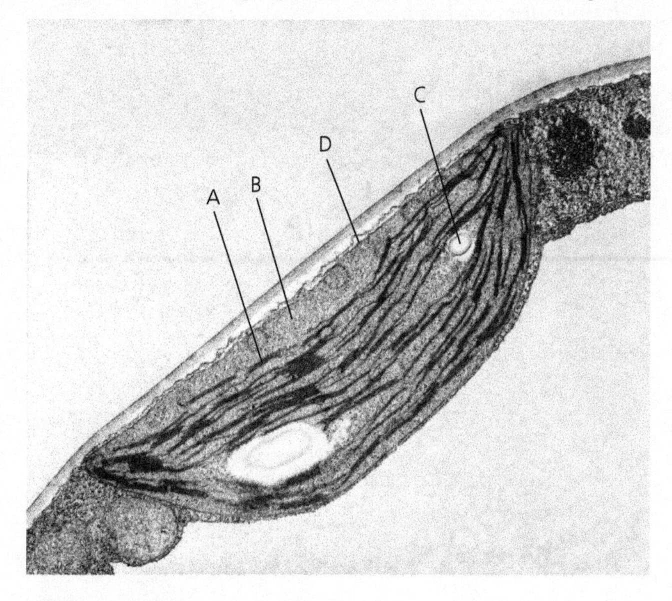

Use the letters on the electron micrograph to complete the following table. You may use the same letter once, more than once or not at all. (2 marks)

Area	Letter
Where chlorophyll is found	
Where carbon dioxide is reduced to a hexose sugar	
Where oxygen is produced from water	
Containing the polysaccharides amylose and amylopectin	

(b) **The enzyme ribulose bisphosphate carboxylase is found in high concentrations within the stroma of the chloroplast.**

(i) **What is the function of this enzyme?** (1 mark)

(ii) **What structures, not shown in the photomicrograph, would need to be present in the chloroplast in order for this enzyme to be synthesised?** (1 mark)

(c) **In order to investigate the light-dependent reactions a suspension of chloroplasts was isolated from an aquatic plant. The chloroplast suspension was kept in the dark and the reagent DCPIP (2,6-dichlorophenol-indophenol) was added. DCPIP is blue when oxidised and colourless when reduced.**

(i) **The suspension of chloroplasts in blue reagent was exposed to sunlight. The blue colour disappeared. Use your knowledge of the light-dependent reactions to explain why.** (2 marks)

(ii) **Another suspension of chloroplasts was set up as before. Small quantities of ADP and inorganic phosphate were added to the suspension and then the tube was exposed to light. The blue colour disappeared more quickly. Explain this observation.** (2 marks)

(iii) **Apart from ADP and P_i, state two variables that would need to be controlled in order for the results to be comparable.** (2 marks)

(d) **In a separate investigation a suspension of algae was supplied with a radioactive isotope of carbon (^{14}C) and allowed to photosynthesise. After a period of time the light was switched off and the algae left in the dark. The graph shows the relative concentrations of some radioactively labelled compounds over the period of the experiment.**

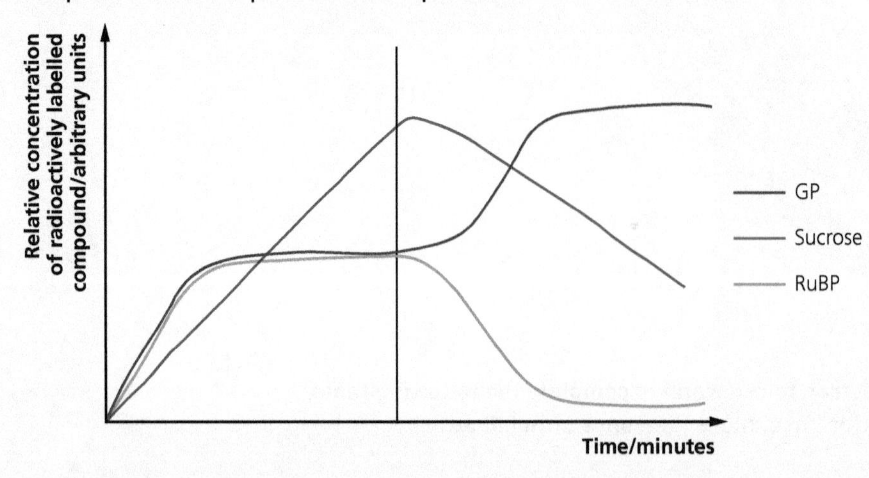

(i) **Explain the changes in the relative concentrations of ribulose bisphosphate (RuBP) and glycerate-3-phosphate after the light was switched off.** (4 marks)

(ii) When the light was switched off the concentration of sucrose changed. What conclusion can be drawn from this observation? Give an explanation for your answer. (2 marks)

Total: 16 marks

e This question is assessing all three assessment objectives, as well as aspects of practical biology. Parts (a) and (b) allow you to demonstrate knowledge and understanding of photosynthesis and chloroplast structure (AO1); these should be easy marks to pick up. The remainder of the question requires you to apply your knowledge and understanding (AO2) of the light-dependent reactions (part (c)) and the light-independent reactions (part (d)). In parts (c) and (d) you are also required to analyse and interpret the information provided to draw conclusions (AO3) as well as develop and refine practical design and procedures (part (ciii)), which also assesses AO3.

Student A

(a) A; B; A; D a

(b) (i) To speed up the light-independent reactions. b

(ii) DNA and ribosomes c

(c) (i) DCPIP turns colourless when it has been reduced, therefore the light must react with the DCPIP and reduce it. d

(ii) ADP and P_i can be used to make ATP; with more ATP the DCPIP is reduced faster. e

(iii) The experiment should be carried out at the same temperature f and with the same volume of DCPIP g.

(d) (i) When the light is switched off the concentration of GP increases and then levels off and the concentration of RuBP decreases then levels off. During the light-independent reactions RuBP combines with CO_2 to make GP. h Therefore, concentration of RuBP decreases and the concentration of GP increases. i

(ii) The concentration of sucrose decreases as it is transported from the leaves to sinks in the phloem. j

e **4/16 marks awarded** a The first three answers are correct, but the last is incorrect — only 1 mark is awarded. b The answer is too vague to gain credit. c Correct. d,e Student A demonstrates a lack of understanding of the process of reduction, and the fact that DCPIP will be reduced if it gains electrons. f Correct. g Although the volume of DCPIP would need to be kept constant, the concentration of DCPIP would have greater impact on the data, so no mark is awarded. h Student A demonstrates knowledge of the light-independent reactions and gains a mark, i but is unable to apply their knowledge to the experimental results. j Incorrect — student A has failed to read the question carefully, and makes references to plants, not algae.

Student B

(a) A; B; A; C a

(b) (i) To catalyse the reaction between ribulose bisphosphate carboxylase and CO_2. b

(ii) DNA and ribosomes c

(c) (i) During the light-dependent reactions a chlorophyll *a* molecule will emit two electrons, which will be accepted by DCPIP and reduce it, turning it colourless. d

(ii) In the first experiment the concentration of ADP and P_i may have been limiting factors, but in the second experiment they weren't limiting the rate. e

(iii) The experiment should be carried out with the same concentration of DCPIP f and with chloroplast suspensions taken from the same source to ensure they both contain the same concentration of chloroplasts g.

(d) (i) When the light is switched off the concentration of GP increases and then levels off. CO_2 is still present so it will combine with RuBP to form GP. h However, without light the light-dependent reactions can't take place so ATP and $NADPH_2$ will not be produced. i Without these GP can't be converted to TP, meaning that RuBP can't be remade. j This explains why the level of RuBP decreases. k

(ii) As the plant is in the dark it will start to respire, causing the concentration of sucrose to decrease. l

e 13/16 marks awarded a All four answers are correct, for 2 marks. b, c Correct. d This gains 1 mark. Student B has correctly identified chlorophyll *a* as the source of electrons to reduce the DCPIP, but has failed to state that the absorption of light energy will cause the electrons to be emitted from the chlorophyll *a* molecules. e Student B has correctly identified ADP and Pi as potential limiting factors, but has failed to link this to ATP synthesis during non-cyclic photophosphorylation. f, g correct. h, i, j, k This is a good answer, clearly demonstrating student B's ability to apply their knowledge and understanding of the light-independent reactions. l Student B has made the correct conclusion about respiration, but fails to gain the second mark — the sucrose would be hydrolysed to glucose and fructose, which would have been used in respiration.

e When preparing for the exams it is important that you revise the relevant subject knowledge, but you also need to review your practical notes, so that you can apply your knowledge and understanding in a practical context. 15% of the marks are awarded for the indirect assessment of practical skills.

The answers provided by student A were vague and demonstrated limited knowledge and understanding of photosynthesis and they lacked the detail expected at this level. The unfamiliar context of the question proved to be too challenging as student A was unable to apply the knowledge they had to the scenario presented. In part (d) (ii) they also failed to read the question carefully. The 4 marks scored are equivalent to a grade U.

In contrast student B has clearly learned the biology and has a good understanding of practical design and procedures. The majority of the answers are concise and well structured, demonstrating an ability to apply knowledge and understanding to an unfamiliar situation. Student B's 13 marks are equivalent to a grade A.

Question 2 Respiration

During respiration the ratio of carbon dioxide produced to oxygen consumed per unit time is known as the respiratory quotient (RQ).

$$RQ = \frac{\text{volume of } CO_2 \text{ evolved}}{\text{volume of } O_2 \text{ consumed}}$$

$$C_6H_{12}O_6 + 6O_2 \rightarrow 6CO_2 + 6H_2O$$

Glucose is the main respiratory substrate and has an RQ value of 1. By looking at the chemical equation for aerobic respiration, it can be seen that six carbon dioxide molecules are produced and six oxygen molecules are consumed. The RQ for this reaction is therefore 6/6 = 1. The respiration of triglycerides gives an RQ of 0.7 and the respiration of protein/amino acids gives an RQ of 0.9.

(a) (i) During which stages of aerobic respiration is carbon dioxide produced? (1 mark)

(ii) Describe the role of oxygen in aerobic respiration. (2 marks)

The diagram below shows the apparatus a student used to investigate the rate of respiration, and the respiratory quotient (RQ), of some maggots. Pressure changes occurring in the boiling tube can be used to calculate the volume of oxygen consumed and carbon dioxide released.

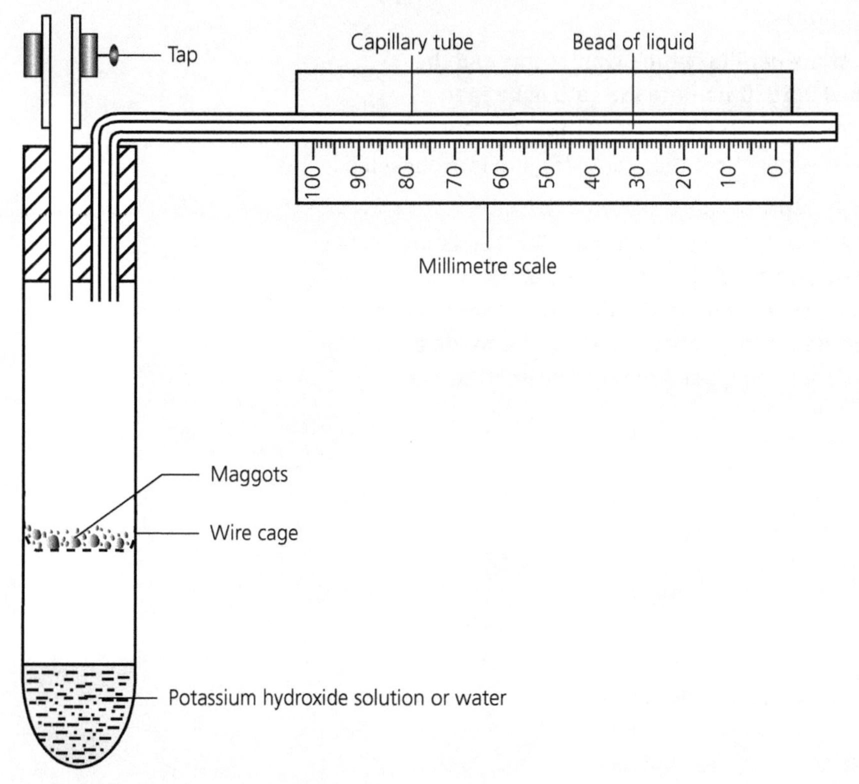

To set up the investigation she used the following method:

- Add 5 cm^3 of potassium hydroxide (KOH) solution to a boiling tube.
- Add 10 maggots to the wire cage and insert it into the boiling tube above the KOH solution. KOH will absorb carbon dioxide from the air.
- Place the bung into the top of the boiling tube with the tap left open.
- Place the assembled apparatus in a water bath at 20°C and leave for 10 minutes.
- Insert a bead of liquid into the capillary tube and close the tap.
- Record the position of the bead of liquid at 1 minute intervals.
- Repeat the experiment using 5 cm^3 of water instead of KOH solution.

The results are shown in the table below.

Time/minutes	Position of the bead of liquid/mm	
	First experiment	Second experiment
0	10	15
1	21	15
2	37	15
3	48	15
4	62	15
5	70	15

(b) (i) Explain why the apparatus was left for 10 minutes, with the tap open, when it was first placed in the water bath. (2 marks)

(ii) From the results of these experiments the student concluded that the maggots were using carbohydrates as a respiratory substrate. Explain how she arrived at this conclusion. (4 marks)

(iii) The cross-sectional area of the capillary tube was 1 mm^2 and the maggots had a total mass of 0.5 g. Calculate the rate of oxygen consumption of the maggots. Give your answer in $mm^3\,g^{-1}\,hour^{-1}$. (2 marks)

(iv) Suggest two limitations in this practical that could lead to inaccuracies in the data collected. (2 marks)

(c) The student repeated the experiment, but used germinating seeds instead of maggots. In the first experiment, with KOH present, the bead of liquid moved 67 mm in 5 minutes. In the second experiment, with water present, the bead of liquid moved 20 mm in 5 minutes. What conclusions can be made about the nature of the respiratory substrate being used in the germinating seeds? (2 marks)

Total: 15 marks

e In this question all three assessment objectives are being assessed as well as your mathematical and practical skills. Part (a) requires you to recall information you have learned during the course (AO1). Parts (b) and (c) require you to apply your knowledge and understanding of respiration in a practical context (AO2); to interpret and evaluate scientific information and evidence to reach conclusions (AO3); and to develop and refine practical design and procedures (AO3). The subject matter of the question is clearly respiration, although this is not a specified practical and you may not have carried it out. However, if you take the time to read through the information provided, you will be able to apply your knowledge and understanding to this particular scenario.

Student A

(a) (i) Krebs cycle a

(ii) Oxygen is the terminal electron acceptor in the electron transport chain. b

(b) (i) To allow the maggots time to get used to being in a boiling tube — if they were anxious their rate of respiration would be higher, but after 10 minutes their rate of respiration would stay the same. c

(ii) In the first experiment the maggots are respiring. This means that they will take in oxygen and the bead of liquid will move towards the boiling tube. All animals use glucose as a respiratory substrate and maggots are animals. In the second experiment, the maggots are not respiring so the bead of liquid doesn't move. d

(iii) The liquid moved 70 mm e in 5 minutes; therefore it would have moved 840 mm in 1 hour.

$840 \times 1\,mm^3 = 840\,mm^3\,g^{-1}\,h^{-1}$ f

(iv) If the bung wasn't put on properly some oxygen could get into the boiling tube. Some of the maggots might have died during the experiment. g

(c) It shows that germinating seeds don't absorb as much oxygen. Because they are plants they can use the oxygen that they can make during photosynthesis. h

e 3/15 marks awarded a Only one stage stated so no mark awarded. b The point made is correct, but student A has failed to state what happens to oxygen — 1 mark awarded. c 1 mark awarded — student A has recognised that the rate of respiration needs to remain constant throughout the investigation. d Student A has failed to read the information clearly and the answer demonstrates a lack of understanding of the experimental set-up. e Student A has been careless when reading off the data in the table, and f has not read the question carefully or taken into account that only 0.5 grams of maggots were present. g One correct limitation identified. h Student A is clearly confused, which suggests they haven't read the information in the stem of the question properly; they are now making the link between seeds and plants, and making incorrect statements about the ability of seeds to photosynthesise.

Student B

(a) (i) Link reaction and the Krebs cycle a

(ii) Oxygen is the terminal electron acceptor in the electron transport chain. It combines with protons and electrons and is reduced to water. b

(b) (i) To allow the temperature of the maggots to reach 20°C, so they are respiring at a constant temperature. A change in temperature will change the volume and therefore the pressure inside the boiling tube. c

(ii) As the maggots respire they will take in oxygen and give out carbon dioxide. In the first experiment the carbon dioxide released is absorbed by the KOH. d This causes the pressure in the boiling tube to decrease, drawing the bead of liquid towards the boiling tube. e In the second experiment there is no pressure change in the boiling tube, so the bead of liquid remains stationary. This shows that the volume of oxygen consumed is the same as the volume of carbon dioxide released. Therefore RQ = 1, so the maggots must be respiring carbohydrates. f

(iii) volume of oxygen consumed by 0.5 g of maggots in 5 minutes = $60 \times 1\,mm^3 = 60\,mm^3$

therefore $60 \times 12 = 720\,mm^3\,h^{-1}$

therefore $720 \times 2 = 1440\,mm^3\,g^{-1}\,h^{-1}$ g

(iv) The apparatus may not be airtight, which would allow gases to enter or escape. The KOH may not absorb all of the CO_2 produced. h

(c) Experiment A shows that '67 mm' represents volume of oxygen consumed. Experiment B shows that '47 mm' of carbon dioxide was produced. RQ = 47/67 = 0.7, therefore triglycerides are being respired. i

e 15/15 marks awarded a, b Both correct. c This demonstrates a clear understanding of the implications on both the physical environment and the organisms involved. d Student B has clearly read all of the information, recognised the significance of KOH and e has clearly linked cause and effect in terms of pressure within the boiling tube. f Student B has again used the information to provide the correct conclusion. g A well-structured answer. h Student B has evaluated the experimental set-up and correctly identified two limitations in the method. i Once again the information provided has been interpreted. Student B has then calculated the correct RQ value and made the correct conclusion from the information provided.

e If you are well prepared and take your time in reading the information provided then questions of this nature shouldn't be too problematic. Student A demonstrated limited knowledge of respiration, failed to use the information provided and was careless in interpreting the data. The 3 marks gained are equivalent to a grade U. In contrast student B, with 15 marks (grade A), has clearly learned the relevant biology and demonstrates a good understanding of practical biology. The answers given are well structured, demonstrating an ability to apply knowledge and understanding to an unfamiliar situation.

Question 3 Microbiology

In 1987 the European Foundation for Environmental Education launched its blue flag programme. The blue flag is awarded for beaches as an indication of their high environmental and quality standards. In order to receive blue flag certification seawater is tested for the presence of pathogenic bacteria, namely *E. coli* and species of the genus *Enterococcus*. *E. coli* is a gram negative bacterium, while *Enterococci* are gram positive. The certificate is only awarded if bathing water contains fewer than 250 *E. coli* and fewer than 100 *Enterococci* per 100 ml.

Describe, and explain, how the two different types of bacteria could be identified and how the numbers of bacteria could be reliably estimated from samples of seawater.

(The quality of your extended response will be assessed in this question) (9 marks QER)

e This question assesses your ability to communicate your ideas clearly and sequentially. The mark scheme for these questions is divided into three bands. An answer that demonstrates limited content, which lacks structure and fails to use correct biological terminology, will be placed in the lower band (1–3 marks). An answer that is articulate and integrated, which correctly links the relevant points and uses correct biological terminology, will be placed in the upper band (7–9 marks). Answers that fall in between these two descriptors are placed in the middle band (4–6 marks).

There are three parts to this question, and all three assessment objectives are being examined. The identification and estimation of bacterial numbers is AO1 (demonstrate knowledge and understanding); however, in this particular context, a serial dilution would be unnecessary (AO2). Aspects of aseptic technique and obtaining reliable estimates bring in the concept of practical design and procedures (AO3).

Student A

The bacteria could be seen as different shapes under the microscope. *Enterococci* are spherical bacteria but *E. coli* aren't. They would also stain different colours — Gram positive bacteria stain purple and gram negative bacteria stain pink. Samples of seawater would need to be diluted down by a factor of 10 and this would be repeated many times. A sample is then transferred to a Petri dish and incubated at 25°C for 24 hours. Some plates will have too many colonies to count and others will have too few. Pick the plate in between these and then count the number of colonies. This number then needs to be multiplied by the dilution factor to give an estimate of the numbers of bacteria in the sea.

e **2/9 marks awarded** Student A makes some relevant points, such as the correct result of the Gram test and how to calculate the number of bacteria; however, there is limited explanation. The answer does address the question, but has omitted any comment on how to ensure that the count would be reliable — this places it in the bottom band. Student A has made limited use of specific biological terminology.

Student B

In order to identify the bacteria the Gram stain could be used. The bacteria would be placed onto a microscope slide and stained with crystal violet. Acetone would then be used to decolorise the bacteria and then safranin would be poured onto the slide. As the *Enterococci* are Gram positive, they would retain the crystal violet and show up as purple. The *E. coli* are gram negative and will stain pink with the safranin.

In order to estimate the number of bacteria sterilised syringes should be used to take samples of seawater from the beach. The samples should be transferred to sterile bottles. 1 cm^3 of the sample should be transferred to a Petri dish containing sterile agar and placed in an incubator for 24 hours. The temperature of the incubator should be 37°C as the bacteria are human pathogenic bacteria. The number of colonies on the plate should then be counted and then multiplied by 100 to calculate the number of bacteria per 100 ml of seawater. This relies on the assumption that a single colony forms from a single bacterium. However, due to the clumping of cells, colonies may merge leading to an underestimation of the numbers of bacteria.

To ensure that the data are reliable several samples of seawater should be taken and tested, so that a mean can be calculated. Aseptic technique would be needed to prevent contamination of the samples and inaccuracies of the results.

e 9/9 marks awarded Student B has given an articulate, integrated account, correctly linking relevant points, which shows sequential reasoning. The answer fully addresses the question and includes the identification of bacteria and the estimation of population number, as well as addressing the concept of reliability. This places it in the top band. Specific biological terminology is used throughout and there are no issues regarding the quality of written communication.

e Although the question is set in an unfamiliar context, the biological knowledge being assessed is quite straightforward. The question states the biology that is required (how to identify the different types of bacteria and make a reliable estimate their numbers) to answer the question in a particular context (cleanliness of seawater). Student A has attempted to answer most parts of the question but the answer shows a limited knowledge of the practical techniques involved. The 2 marks gained are equivalent to a grade E. In contrast student B has given a detailed account, clearly demonstrating ability to recall and apply knowledge of practical microbiology. The 9 marks awarded (grade A) show that student B was well prepared and had spent time learning the biology required.

Question 4 Population size and ecosystems

Leghaemoglobin is a protein found in the root nodules of leguminous plants. It is produced by legumes in response to the roots being colonised by nitrogen-fixing bacteria as part of the symbiotic interaction between plant and bacterium. Leghaemoglobin has close chemical and structural similarities to haemoglobin and, like haemoglobin, is red in colour.

Nitrogenases are enzymes used by some bacteria to convert atmospheric nitrogen gas (N_2) into ammonia. The ammonia can then be utilised by the bacterium. Nitrogenases are oxygen-sensitive and the presence of oxygen reduces the efficiency of the enzyme.

(a) (i) Name the genus of bacteria that form a symbiotic relationship with leguminous plants. (1 mark)

(ii) State two reasons why the bacteria require a source of nitrogen. (1 mark)

(b) **If these symbiotic bacteria are isolated from root nodules and grown in the laboratory their ability to convert nitrogen gas to ammonia is greatly reduced. Use the information provided to explain how the symbiotic relationship benefits both the bacteria and the leguminous plant.** (3 marks)

(c) ***Azotobacter* are free-living in the soil and have the ability to fix atmospheric nitrogen. They also have an extremely high metabolic rate. Use your knowledge of respiration to explain how the metabolic rate of the bacterium enables it to fix atmospheric nitrogen.** (2 marks)

(d) **The Venus flytrap (*Dionaea muscipula*) is an American species of carnivorous plant found growing in waterlogged soils. The plant is able to trap and digest insects. Suggest why this is vital to the survival of the plants.** (2 marks)

(e) **The diagram below shows the levels of ammonia, nitrite and nitrate in the water of a closed aquarium (fish tank), containing five fish.**

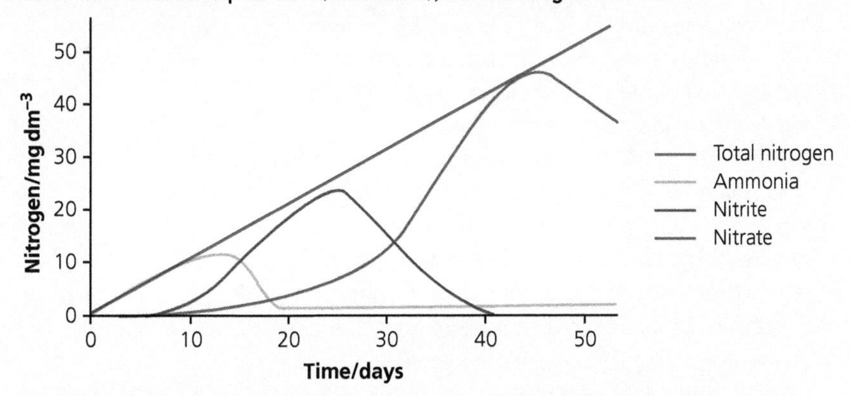

(i) **Describe and explain the changes in the concentration of ammonia, nitrite and nitrate from the time it was set up until day 40.** (3 marks)

(ii) **The graph shows that that around day 50 the levels of nitrate start to decrease, however the levels of total nitrogen continued to increase. Suggest an explanation to account for this observation.** (1 mark)

Total: 13 marks

(e) This question is concerned with different aspects of the nitrogen cycle, but asked in novel contexts, so it is mainly assessing AO2 (apply knowledge and understanding). Part (a) requires you to simply recall information you have learned about the nitrogen cycle (AO1). Parts (b) and (c) contain synoptic elements and incorporate knowledge of haemoglobin and respiration, requiring you to apply this knowledge and understanding in the context provided (AO2). Parts (b), (c) and (e)(ii) require you to analyse, interpret and evaluate the information to reach conclusions (AO3).

Student A

(a) **(i)** Nitrogen-fixing bacteria [a]

(ii) So that plants can produce amino acids and proteins. [b]

(b) The bacteria will produce ammonia from nitrogen gas and give some to the plant. The plant provides the bacteria with somewhere to live and will give them shelter and food, for example glucose. [c]

(c) Oxygen is needed for respiration. The high rate of respiration will keep the oxygen concentration low. d

(d) The Venus flytrap can digest the insects and absorb the products of digestion. e Therefore it doesn't need to be able to photosynthesise.

(e) **(i)** The waste produced by fish will be decomposed and ammonia is produced. The ammonia is then converted to nitrites and nitrates by nitrifying bacteria. f

(ii) The owner put some plants into the tank and they started to absorb the nitrates. g

2/13 marks awarded a The term nitrogen-fixing bacteria is written in the stem of the question. Part (a) clearly states that it is the 'name of the genus' that is required. b Amino acids are used to synthesise proteins, and so only one reason has been given. c 1 mark awarded, for correctly stating that the plant would obtain ammonia from the bacteria. However, the rest of the statement is vague — student A would have gained an additional mark if they had made reference to the use of glucose in respiration. d No marks awarded — student A has demonstrated a limited knowledge of respiration and hasn't explained why the low oxygen concentration is beneficial to the bacterium. e Again this is a vague answer, which makes no link between waterlogged soils and diminished access to nitrates. The second sentence is incorrect. f Although student A has recognised the relevant parts of the nitrogen cycle required to answer the question, their response lacks detail and doesn't make reference to the graph, so no marks are awarded. g This is a plausible suggestion, and explains the fall in nitrate concentration — 1 mark awarded.

Student B

(a) **(i)** *Rhizobium* a

(ii) Nitrogen is needed so the plants can synthesise amino acids and nucleic acids. b

(b) The leghaemoglobin has a high affinity for oxygen and so will associate with it. This is beneficial to the bacteria as it prevents the oxygen inhibiting the nitrogenase enzymes, allowing the conversion of nitrogen gas into ammonia. c

(c) Oxygen is the terminal electron acceptor in the electron transport chain and is reduced to water. As oxygen is used in respiration it can't inhibit nitrogenase. d

(d) Waterlogged soils encourage denitrification, so the concentration of nitrates in the soils would be low. The Venus flytrap can digest the insects to obtain the nitrates they need. e

(e) **(i)** Fish excrete ammonia through their gills, causing the concentration of ammonia to increase. Ammonia will also be produced by saprophytic bacteria during the decomposition of fish faeces and uneaten food.

Nitrifying bacteria, such as *Nitrosomonas* will convert the ammonia into nitrites, which results in the decrease of ammonia and the increase in nitrites around day 10. *Nitrobacter* (also a type of nitrifying bacteria) will convert these nitrites into nitrates, which results in the decrease of nitrites and the increase in nitrates around day 28. f

(ii) Algae started to grow in the tank. They absorbed the nitrates and converted them into organic molecules, such as amino acids. g

e 10/13 marks awarded a, b Correct. c 2 marks awarded — this is an excellent explanation of the role of leghaemoglobin and how this will benefit the bacterium. Unfortunately student B failed to state the benefit of the relationship to the plant. d 1 mark awarded for describing the role of oxygen in respiration; however, the second sentence is vague and fails to make the connection between the high metabolic rate and the lowering of oxygen concentration in the cell. e 1 mark for making the link between waterlogged soils and denitrification. To gain the second mark student B needed to refer to the 'digestion of insect proteins' acting as a source of 'amino acids' — they do not act as a source of nitrates. f An excellent, well-structured answer for all 3 marks, demonstrating knowledge of the nitrogen cycle and linking it to the data provided. g Correct.

e If you are well prepared you should be able to gain most of the marks available on this type of question. Student A failed to read the question carefully and lost some easy marks. They had clearly learned the biology required to score marks in part (e) but the answers lacked the detail and precise use of terminology expected at this level. 2 marks are equivalent to a grade U. In contrast student B has clearly learned the biology of the nitrogen cycle and interpreted the information provided, giving concise and well-structured answers. They have clearly demonstrated an ability to apply their knowledge and understanding to the unfamiliar situations given, gaining 11 marks (grade A).

Question 5 The kidney

Some brain tumours or head injuries that result in damage to the pituitary gland can lead to a condition called diabetes insipidus. Diabetes insipidus is not related to diabetes mellitus (usually just known as diabetes), but it does share some of the same signs and symptoms, such as thirst and passing large amounts of urine. In very severe cases of diabetes insipidus, up to 20 litres of urine can be passed in a day.

(a) **A diagram of a kidney nephron is shown on the next page.**

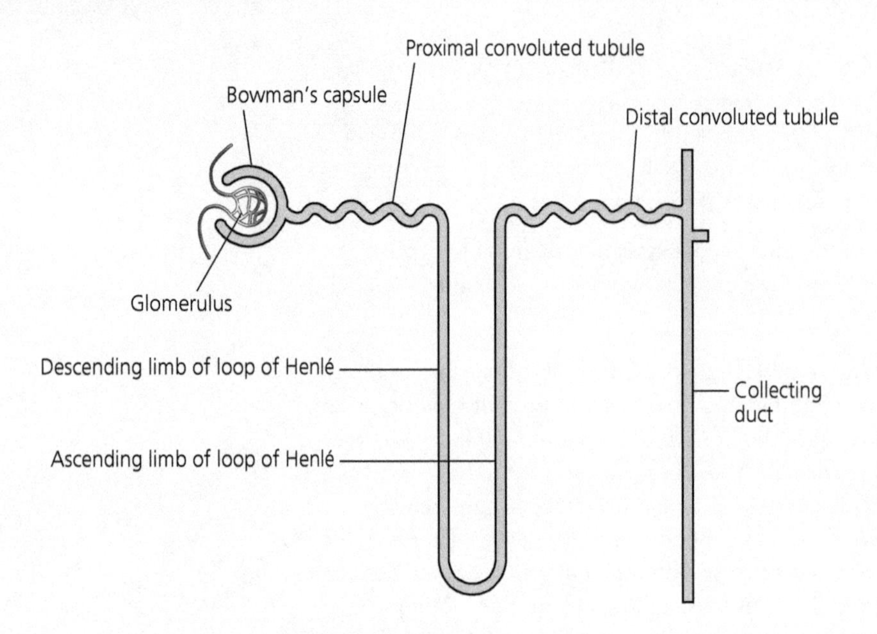

Describe the process of ultrafiltration. (4 marks)

(b) **Approximately 1200 cm^3 of blood passes through the glomerular capillaries every minute. In a healthy individual 125 cm^3 of fluid is filtered from this blood into the renal capsules, resulting in 1500 cm^3 of urine being produced each day.**

(i) **Calculate the volume of filtrate, in cm^3, produced by the kidneys in a day. Give your answer in standard form.** (2 marks)

(ii) **Calculate the percentage of the filtrate that is reabsorbed into the bloodstream. Give your answer to three significant figures.** (2 marks)

(c) **Use your knowledge of osmoregulation to explain the symptoms associated with the condition.** (3 marks)

(d) **The analysis of urine samples can also help with the diagnosis of certain medical conditions.**

- **People who suffer from type I diabetes (diabetes mellitus) are unable to produce insulin. Insulin is responsible for converting excess glucose into glycogen.**
- **In nephrosis the basement membrane of the Bowman's capsule becomes permeable to large molecules that would not normally leave the plasma.**
- **In obstructive jaundice the bile duct becomes blocked, so that the constituents of bile spill into the blood and subsequently enter the urine.**

The table below shows the results of some biochemical tests carried out on urine samples from four different individuals.

Urine sample	Result after testing with		
	Benedict's reagent	Powdered sulfur*	Biuret reagent
A	Blue	Floated	Violet
B	Blue	Sank	Blue
C	Red	Floated	Blue
D	Blue	Floated	Blue

* Powdered sulfur sinks rapidly in water if emulsifiers are present

All four individuals were diagnosed with medical conditions. Using all of the information provided, what conclusions can be made regarding the results of the urine analysis? (4 marks)

Total: 15 marks

ⓔ This is a fairly straightforward question regarding kidney function; however, there is a lot of information for you to process. Part (b) requires you to recall the process of ultrafiltration (AO1 — demonstrate knowledge and understanding). Part (b) is assessing your mathematical skills (AO2), while part (c) requires you to apply your knowledge and understanding of osmoregulation (AO2). Part (d) requires you to analyse the scientific information provided to reach conclusions (AO3). There is also a synoptic element here, requiring you to draw on your knowledge of biochemical tests and digestion.

Student A

(a) Blood enters the glomerulus under high hydrostatic pressure, which forces fluid out of the capillaries and into the Bowman's capsule. Only water and small molecules such as urea are forced out. Red blood cells and plasma proteins are too big, so they stay in the capillary. a

(b) (i) $125 \times 60 \times 24 = 180\,000\,\text{cm}^3$ b

(ii) $(180\,000 - 1500)/180\,000 = 99.16\%$ reabsorbed c

(c) When someone is dehydrated ADH is secreted from the pituitary gland and increases the permeability of the walls of the collecting duct to water. This results in more water being reabsorbed from the filtrate and the person produces small volumes of concentrated urine. Someone with this disease can't do this. d

(d) Urine sample A contains protein so the person has high blood pressure. e

Urine sample B contains emulsifiers. f

Urine sample C contains glucose so the person has type I diabetes. g

Sample D came from a healthy person as all three tests came back negative. h

ⓔ **4/15 marks awarded** a The answer lacks detail and only demonstrates a limited knowledge of ultrafiltration. It conveys the idea that ultrafiltration forces small molecules out of the plasma, with large molecules remaining, so gains 1 mark. b Student A has carried out the correct calculation but has not expressed the volume of filtrate in standard form, or c given the volume of fluid reabsorbed to three significant figures; 1 mark is awarded for each part. d Student A has demonstrated an understanding of the process of osmoregulation, but has failed to apply this to the medical condition, and therefore gained no marks. In the final part of the question student A has failed to process all of the information provided.

e They have correctly interpreted the result of the Biuret test, but then drawn the wrong conclusion. f They have failed to link the presence of emulsifiers to any medical condition. g Correct. h They have drawn the wrong conclusion.

Student B

(a) Blood enters the glomerulus under high hydrostatic pressure. This is due to ventricular systole and the effect of the efferent arteriole being narrower than the afferent arterioles, causing blood to 'back-up' in the glomerular capillaries. Fluid is forced out of the glomerulus, through the pores in the capillary wall, the basement membrane and between the 'foot-like' processes of the podocytes, into the Bowman's capsule. The basement membrane, surrounding the capillaries, acts as a molecular filter. Water and small molecules, such as glucose and urea, are forced out of the blood plasma, while cells and large molecules, such as plasma proteins, remain in the capillaries. a

(b) (i) $125 \times 60 \times 24 = 180000 = 1.8 \times 10^5 cm^3$ b

(ii) $(1500/180000) \times 100 = 0.833\%$ urine produced

Therefore (99.167%) 99.2% of fluid is reabsorbed. c

(c) If the pituitary gland is damaged then ADH will not be secreted and the walls of the collecting duct will remain impermeable to water. Less water will be reabsorbed back into the bloodstream and large volumes of dilute urine will be produced. d

(d) Urine sample A tested positive with Biuret reagent, so protein is present in the urine. The pores in the basement membrane are too small to allow the passage of proteins into the filtrate, so this person may suffer from nephrosis. e

Powdered sulfur sank in urine sample B, indicating that emulsifiers are present. Bile salts are involved in digestion and emulsify lipids in the duodenum, so this sample may have come from someone with obstructive jaundice. f

Urine sample C tested positive with Benedict's reagent, so reducing sugars are present in the urine. Glucose is a reducing sugar, and is normally reabsorbed in the proximal convoluted tubule, so this sample may have come from someone with type I diabetes. g

Sample D came back negative for all three tests. This individual may be suffering from diabetes insipidus. h

e **15/15 marks awarded** a Student B has provided a coherent answer that demonstrates a detailed knowledge of the process of ultrafiltration, gaining all 4 marks. b, c Correct. d This demonstrates a good understanding of the process of osmoregulation, resulting in a clear, concise answer, which gains all 3 marks. e, f, g, h In the final part of the question student B has correctly interpreted the result of the biochemical test, and then drawn the correct conclusions using the information provided.

ⓔ Student A made some careless mistakes and should have gained more marks. The answers also lacked the detail and precise use of terminology that is expected at this level. The 4 marks gained are equivalent to a grade U. In contrast, student B gains full marks (grade A) for demonstrating good knowledge and understanding of the function of the nephron. As well as using the information provided, student B has applied their knowledge and drawn the correct conclusions. The answers provided are coherent and include the terminology expected at this level.

Question 6 The nervous system

(a) **When a person steps on a nail, the leg that is stepping on the nail pulls away, while the other leg takes the weight of the whole body, this is called the crossed extensor reflex. During this reflex an impulses passes from a receptor to the spinal cord on one side of the body and leaves via a motor neurone, which causes a muscle to contract on the opposite side of the body.**

Figure 1 is a diagram of a section of the spinal cord.

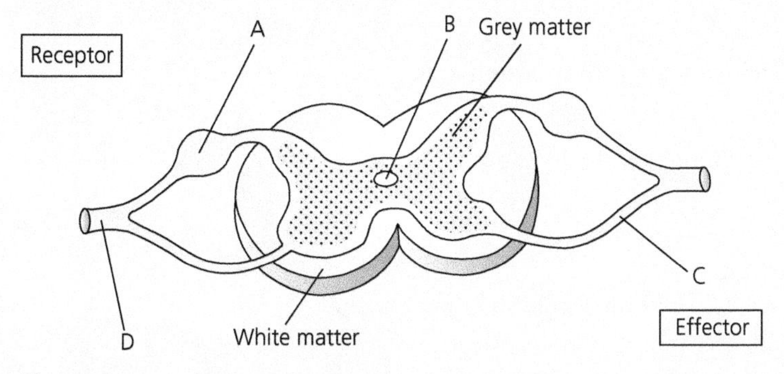

Figure 1

(i) **Identify structures A–D.** (2 marks)

(ii) **On Figure 1, draw a sensory neurone, a relay neurone and a motor neurone. The sensory neurone should enter at one side of the spinal cord and the motor neurone should exit on the other side. The neurones should link the receptor to the effector. Label each neurone.** (3 marks)

(b) **Figure 2 shows a mechanoreceptor, called a Pacinian corpuscle, which is found in the skin. It consists of a single sensory neurone surrounded by layers of connective tissue filled with a viscous gel. It responds to changes in pressure. When Pacinian corpuscles are stimulated the voltage across the membrane of the terminal dendrite is briefly reversed and a generator potential is produced. The sodium-gated channels in the membrane respond to deformations in the membrane. Once a receptor potential has been established action potentials are transmitted along the sensory neurone.**

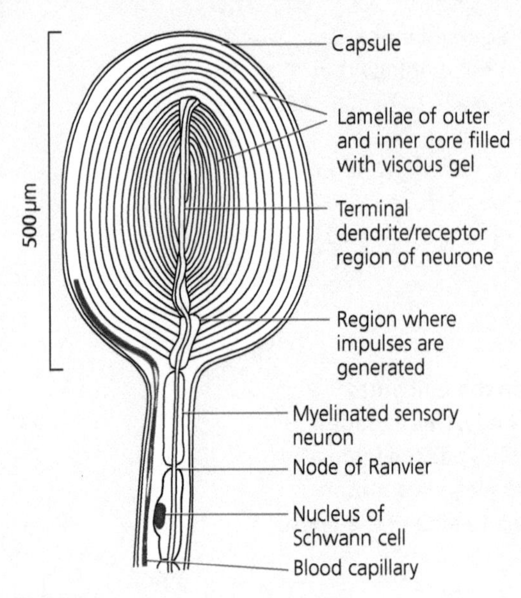

Figure 2

Use the information provided to explain how a generator potential is produced when an object is touched. (3 marks)

(c) Figure 3 shows the sequence of changes that occur during application and removal of a pressure stimulus in:

- **the shape of the Pacinian corpuscle**
- **the deformation of the nerve membrane**
- **the size of the generator potential, in the receptor region of the neurone (terminal dendrite)**
- **the discharge of nerve impulses in the sensory neurone leading from the corpuscle**

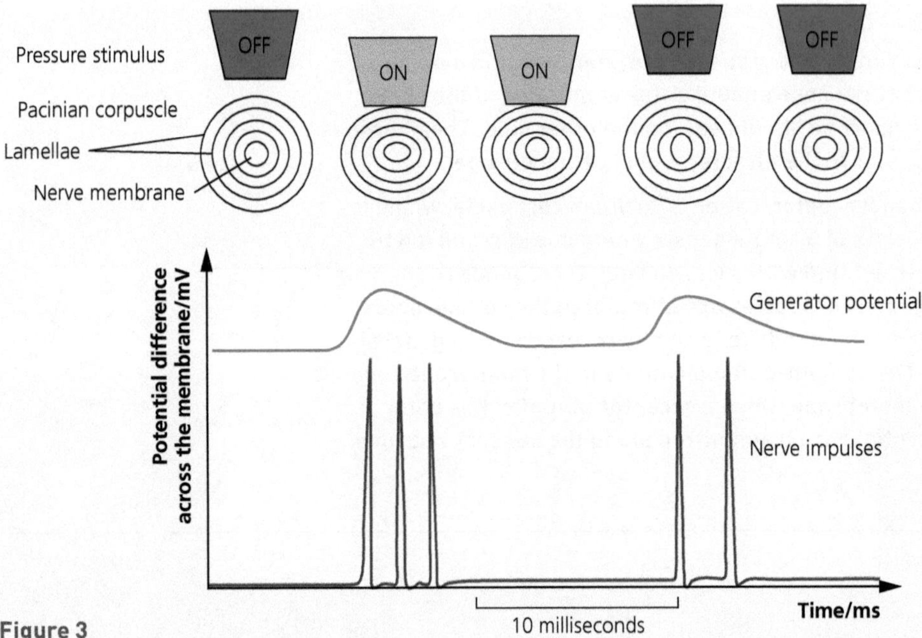

Figure 3

Use the information provided to explain how changes in pressure are detected, and how the information is transmitted to the central nervous system. (5 marks)

Total: 13 marks

ⓔ Questions on the nervous system involving spinal reflexes are common and many students lose marks when asked to complete diagrams showing the nerves involved. The spinal cord can be shown orientated in different ways and you must make sure that you use any information given in the text. Part (a) requires you to demonstrate knowledge and understanding (AO1) and the marks are relatively easy to gain if you are well prepared, and read the question carefully. In part (b) you are required to apply your knowledge and understanding of action potentials to answer the question about generator potentials (AO2). Part (c) is very challenging because it provides experimental data in an unfamiliar context, and requires you to apply your knowledge and understanding, as well as interpret the information provided to draw conclusions (AO3). Note that part (c) is worth 5 marks so you need to make sure that you provide a detailed answer.

Student A

(a) (i) A= motor neurone, B = central canal, C = ventral root, D = dorsal root a

(ii) b

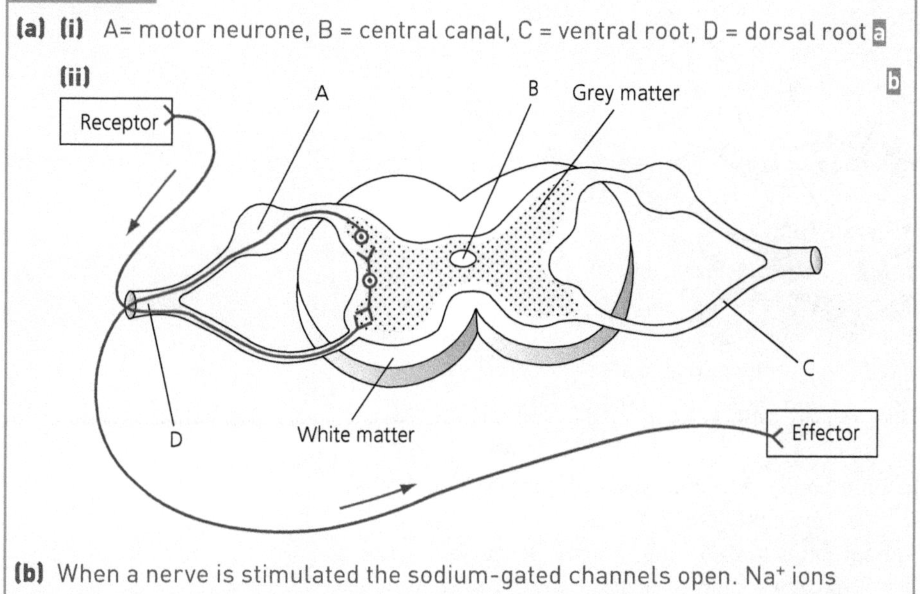

(b) When a nerve is stimulated the sodium-gated channels open. Na^+ ions move into the axon causing the inside to become positively charged. c

(c) When the pressure is on, the Pacinian corpuscle is squashed and a generator potential is produced. This sends three nerve impulses along the sensory neurone. When the pressure is taken off another generator potential is produced and two nerve impulses are sent along the sensory neurone. d

ⓔ **2/13 marks awarded** a A and D are labelled incorrectly; B and C are correct, for 1 mark. b Student A has ignored the information provided and attempted to draw a normal reflex pathway. However, the sensory neurone and motor neurone are entering and leaving the spinal cord via the wrong roots and no credit can be given for the relay neurone as no labels have been provided. c This is a vague answer, and it would appear that the student is recalling information on action potentials and not applying their knowledge. They have failed to process the information provided and therefore the answer lacks explanation. They also make reference to axons, when 'terminal dendrite' is labelled on the diagram. d Student A has shown limited skill in interpreting the diagram. They have failed to make reference to the change in the shape of the terminal dendrite and the effect this would have on the permeability of the membrane to Na^+. They have also failed to recognise that the two generator potentials differ in size and that this affects the frequency of nerve impulses sent along the sensory neurone. 1 mark is awarded for recognising that impulses would be generated when pressure is applied and removed.

Student B

(a) (i) A= dorsal root ganglion, B = central canal, C = ventral root, D = connective tissue a

(ii) b

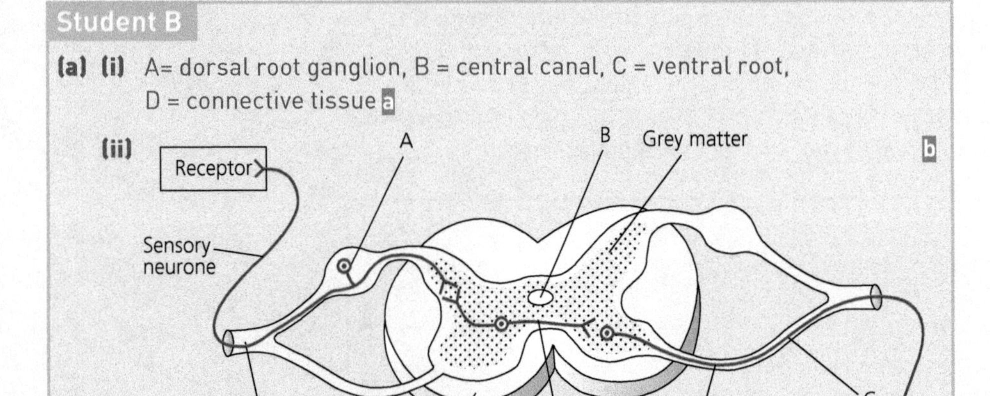

(b) When an object is touched, pressure is applied to the Pacinian corpuscle, causing the membrane of the terminal dendrite to be deformed. This will result in the opening of sodium-gated channels. Na^+ will rapidly diffuse into the terminal dendrite, causing the inside of the dendrite to become positively charged. c

(c) When pressure is applied the neurone membrane is deformed. A generator potential is established in the terminal dendrite and nerve impulses are transmitted along the sensory neurone. When the pressure is removed the neurone membrane is once again deformed and a generator potential is again established in the terminal dendrite and nerve impulses are transmitted along the sensory neurone. This generator potential is smaller than the first and results in fewer nerve impulses being transmitted along the sensory neurone. d

e **10/13 marks awarded** a Labels A, B and C are correct for 1 mark; both students failed to recognise D as a spinal nerve. b Student B has used the information provided and correctly drawn the position of, and labelled, the three neurones. c This answer clearly demonstrates student B's ability to apply their knowledge to the situation presented. They have processed the information and given a concise answer — 3 marks awarded. **d** Student B has recognised, and explained, why generator potentials and nerve impulses are established when pressure is both applied and removed, for 3 marks. Unfortunately they haven't made reference to all of the diagram; during continuous stimulation the nerve membrane, once distorted, remains distorted. As the membrane structure remains the same no generator potentials, or nerve impulses, are generated.

e There will always be questions that contain information about unfamiliar situations. However, if you take your time reading the information, you will be able to pick out the relevant biology that you have learned and therefore be able to gain the majority of the marks. Student A has shown a complete lack of knowledge and understanding of the nervous system and has failed to pick up the 'easy' marks. The 2 marks awarded are equivalent to a grade U. Student B gains 10 marks (grade A) for analysing the data and providing detailed, coherent answers. They have clearly spent time learning the biology that they were taught and have demonstrated the ability to apply this knowledge in a novel context.

Knowledge check answers

1 By containing several pigments the chloroplast can absorb a greater range of wavelengths of light, therefore absorbing more light energy, increasing the rate of photosynthesis.

2 Plants appear green as the green wavelengths of light are reflected by the photosynthetic pigments.

3 On the thylakoid membranes

4 a The reaction centre
 b The antenna complex

5 ATP and $NADPH_2$

6 a Yellow pigment: Rf value = 19 mm/68 mm = 0.28
 b The orange pigment is carotene; the blue-green pigment is chlorophyll *a*; the yellow-green pigment is chlorophyll *b*; the yellow pigment is xanthophyll.

7 The metabolic pathway does not involve oxygen.

8 The glucose molecules cannot enter the mitochondria and as the mitochondria have been isolated from the cell there are no enzymes present to convert the glucose into pyruvate.

9 Oxygen is the terminal electron acceptor in the electron transport chain. It accepts electrons and protons and is reduced to water; this allows the coenzymes NAD and FAD to be regenerated.

10 a Any two molecules from pyruvate, $NADH_2$, ADP or inorganic phosphate (P_i)
 b Any two molecules from water, NAD or ATP

11 a The rate of ATP synthesis would increase. The enzymes involved in glycolysis, the link reaction and Krebs cycle would have more kinetic energy and would therefore increase the rate of the reactions involved. This would result in more $NADH_2$ and $FADH_2$ being produced, leading to more ATP being produced via oxidative phosphorylation. More ATP would also be produced via substrate-level phosphorylation during glycolysis and the Krebs cycle.
 b The rate of ATP synthesis would fall. Less ATP would be produced via substrate-level phosphorylation during the Krebs cycle. Less ATP would be produced via oxidative phosphorylation as less $NADH_2$ and $FADH_2$ would be produced during the link reaction and Krebs cycle.

12 a Oxygen
 b Pyruvate
 c Ethanal

13 Its cells are spherical and it has a simple cell wall composed of a thick layer of peptidoglycan.

14 Carbon: to be able to synthesise organic molecules.
Nitrogen: to be able to synthesise amino acids, proteins and nucleic acids.
Phosphorus: to be able to synthesise nucleotides and nucleic acids such as ATP, DNA and RNA.

15 Gram negative: it has a complex cell wall composed of a thin layer of peptidoglycan and an outer layer of lipopolysaccharides; these bacteria stain pink as the cell wall does not retain the crystal violet stain.
Facultative anaerobe: they grow better in the presence of oxygen but can survive in anaerobic conditions.

16 19 colonies counted from a dilution factor of 10^{-4}; $19 \times 10^4 = 190\,000$ or 1.9×10^5 bacteria.

17 A total count includes both living and dead cells and can therefore overestimate the population. A viable count includes only living cells and is based on the assumption that one cell gives rise to one colony. However if there is clumping of cells then the colonies will merge, giving an underestimate of the population.

18 The lag phase in the rat population is caused by a low number of individuals of reproductive age. The lag phase in the yeast population is due to the switching on of genes and the synthesis of the necessary enzymes to allow the yeast cells to utilise their culture medium.

19 Carrying capacity is the maximum population that the environment can support indefinitely. Exponential growth occurs when the population size doubles per unit time.

20 Density-dependent factors include competition for food/water/mates, predation, disease and the accumulation of toxic waste. Density-independent factors include climatic factors such as temperature.

21 It is acting in a density-independent manner as 20% of the beetles are dying at each population density.

22 In broad-leafed woodland the two species are in direct competition and the grey squirrels have outcompeted the red squirrels, which have become locally extinct.

23 Secondary production in primary consumers = $(13\,472/83\,240) \times 100 = 16.2\%$

24 Carnivores have high-protein diets, whereas herbivores have high-cellulose diets. As protein is easier to digest, a higher percentage of the food consumed by a carnivore is broken down, compared with that consumed by a herbivore.

25 a To produce 1 kg of herbivore, 10 kg of plant matter would be required.
 b To produce 1 kg of carnivore, 10 kg of herbivore and therefore 100 kg of plant matter would be required.
 c As more energy is lost along the food chain, meat from a carnivorous animal would be very expensive to produce and therefore buy.

26 The nitrates provide a source of nitrogen to synthesise amino acids/proteins and nucleotides/nucleic acids.

27 a Draining waterlogged fields reduces anaerobic conditions and therefore reduces denitrification by denitrifying bacteria.
 b Ploughing fields aerates the soil so that nitrifying bacteria can convert ammonium ions into nitrates for plant growth.

c Planting of leguminous crops such as clover allows nitrogen-fixing bacteria to convert atmospheric nitrogen into ammonium ions.

d Ploughing of crops such as clover into the soil encourages putrefaction by saprophytic bacteria, which increases the concentration of ammonium ions (and ultimately nitrate ions) in the soil.

28 Artificial fertilisers contain nitrates, which are highly soluble and therefore easily leached from the soil. Manure contains nitrogen-containing organic molecules, such as proteins and nucleic acids, which must be broken down and converted to nitrates.

29 a Mean number of buttercups per quadrat: 49/10 = 4.9

b Mean number of buttercups per m^2: each quadrat measures $0.25\,m^2$, therefore $4.9 \times 4 = 19.6\,m^{-2}$

30 Biodiversity is the number of species and the number of individuals of each species in a given area.

31 A decrease in photosynthesis results in less CO_2 being removed from the atmosphere and the combustion of wood releases CO_2 into the atmosphere.

32 This allows the juvenile fish to escape the nets. They are allowed to mature and reproduce, leading to an increase in the fish population.

33 Although they have access to fresh water they excrete uric acid. They are reptiles and therefore lay eggs. The low toxicity of uric acid means that it can accumulate inside the eggs without damaging the embryos.

34 The efferent arteriole has a narrower lumen than the afferent arteriole, which causes a build-up of blood in the capillaries and increases the hydrostatic pressure.

35 a Any three from: water, glucose, amino acids, urea, fatty acids, glycerol, small proteins, inorganic ions (e.g. Na^+)

b Large plasma proteins

36 The microvilli provide a large surface area for absorption and they contain many mitochondria to provide ATP for active transport.

37 The otter is a mammal that lives in/around fresh water. It therefore has short loops of Henle as it does not need to produce urine with a low water potential. The camel is a mammal that lives in deserts. It has very long loops of Henle. This generates a very high solute concentration in the tissues of the medulla, enabling the camel to reabsorb more water.

38 The loop of Henle

39 The receptors (detectors) are the osmoreceptors in the hypothalamus; the coordinator is the posterior lobe of the pituitary gland (and ADH); the effectors are the walls of the distal convoluted tubule and collecting ducts of the nephron.

40 If both fluids travelled in the same direction the concentration of urea would reach equilibrium part way along the machine. Once equilibrium is reached no more diffusion of urea from the blood plasma would occur. In countercurrent exchange equilibrium is never reached. Therefore the concentration of urea in the blood plasma is always higher than the concentration of urea in the dialysate. This results in urea diffusing from the blood into the dialysate for the entire length of the machine, so that more urea is removed from the blood plasma.

41 Muscles and glands

42 An axon transmits impulses away from the cell body; a dendrite transmits impulses towards the cell body.

43 The Na^+/K^+ pump actively transports three Na^+ ions out of the axon in exchange for two K^+ ions. The membrane of the axon is more permeable to K^+ ions so they diffuse out more rapidly than the Na^+ ions. This creates an uneven distribution of charge and the membrane is polarised, with the inside of the axon being negatively charged.

44 When the neurone is stimulated the sodium channels open, increasing the permeability of the membrane to Na^+. The Na^+ ions diffuse rapidly into the axon, depolarising the membrane, with the inside of the axon becoming positively charged.

45 a The myelin sheath provides electrical insulation to the neurone by preventing ion exchange across the membrane. Depolarisations can only occur at the nodes of Ranvier, which cause the current to flow further along the axon, increasing the length of local circuits. The action potential moves by saltatory conduction, which speeds up the transmission of the nerve impulse.

b The increase in diameter reduces the longitudinal resistance of the cytoplasm in the axon. This increases the length of the local circuits and the distance between adjacent depolarisations along the axon, increasing the speed of transmission.

46 The mitochondria provide ATP for the resynthesis of neurotransmitter and for the Na^+/K^+ pump.

47 Synapses only transmit impulses in one direction because the neurotransmitter is found on the presynaptic side and the neurotransmitter receptors are found on the postsynaptic membrane. The refractory period prevents the nerve impulse from travelling in two directions along an axon.

48 The insecticide is an excitatory drug. It inhibits acetylcholinesterase and therefore acetylcholine cannot be broken down. The acetylcholine remains in the synapse and causes continuous stimulation of the postsynaptic membrane.

49 White matter contains myelinated axons; the grey matter is composed of cell bodies.

50

Stimulus	Hot surface
Receptor	Thermoreceptors and pain receptors in the skin
Co-ordinator	CNS (spinal cord)
Effector	Arm (biceps) muscles
Response	Contraction of muscle to remove the hand/arm

51

Nerve net	Vertebrate neurones
Only one type of neurone	Three types of neurone
Neurones are shorter	Neurons are longer
Neurones branched	Neurones not branched
Neurones can transmit impulses in both directions	Neurones can transmit impulses in one direction only
Impulses pass in all directions from point of stimulation	Impulses follow a unidirectional pathway from the point of stimulation
Neurones are non-myelinated	Neurones may be myelinated
Many synapses involved	Few synapses involved
Slower transmission of impulses	Faster transmission of impulses

Note: **bold** page numbers indicate key term definitions.